My Childhood
at the Gate of Unrest

by Paul Goma

**translated from Romanian
by Angela Clark**

readers international

The title of this book in Romanian is *Din Calidor: o copilarie in Basarabia*, first published in French as *Le Calidor* in 1987 by Editions Albin Michel. Published in Romanian by *Dialog* in the Federal Republic of Germany.
© Editions Albin Michel S.A. 1987

First published in English by Readers International Inc, Columbia, Louisiana and Readers International, London. Editorial inquiries to the London office at 8 Strathray Gardens, London NW3 4NY, England. US/Canadian inquiries to the Subscriber Service Dept, P O Box 959, Columbia LA 71418-0959, USA.

English translation © Readers International Inc 1990
This translation was made possible in part through grants from the Wheatland Foundation, New York, and the Central & East European Publishing Project, Oxford.

Cover illustration, *Peasant Life* (1925) by Marc Chagall, courtesy of the Albright-Knox Art Gallery, Buffalo NY, USA.
Cover design by Jan Brychta.
Printed and bound in Malta by Interprint Limited.

Library of Congress Catalog Card Number: 89-64268
British Library Cataloguing in Publication Data
    Goma, Paul, *1935-*
    My Childhood at the Gate of Unrest.
    I. Title II. Din Calidor. *English*
    859.334

ISBN 0-930523-73-3 Hardcover
ISBN 0-930523-74-1 Paperback

My Childhood
at the Gate of Unrest

Preface

The gallery outside my parents' house in Mana was the hub of the universe.

For me, all things take their departure from that place and from that time and, after leaving definitively, after wide and perfectly circular detours, they all arrive back at that time and that place.

I said gallery to give you a picture of what I'm talking about; but in fact what the house had we didn't call a gallery, nor balcony nor porch, nor any peasant Slavicism, nor verandah nor any provincial Turkism either. Our house had a *calidor.*

Although Father had explained to me in a learned way, as befitted a country schoolteacher, where and how the word came to us (from French via Russian), and although later, at university, I came to accept the linguistic evidence: the French *corridor* became in Russian *karidor,* in which form it entered russified Basarabia where, in Romanian, it was...palatalized - the etymology propounded by Mother from the very beginning was so much more attractive that it really *had* to be the true one:

"*Calidor*, that is, *sublime longing.*"

Or, in other words, the Greek *kali* and the Romanian *dor*, a longing which, from 1812 onwards, was expressed in songs and in sighs between the Dniester and the Prut* more

*Basarabia (called *Bessarabia* by the Russians) is the territory between the Dniester river to the east and the Prut river to the west, originally a part of Moldavia in Romanian territory. In 1812 the territory was ceded to Russia by Romania's Turkish rulers. It was returned to Romania after World War I but was annexed by the USSR in 1940. The river Prut now forms the frontier between modern Romania and the Soviet Union. [This and other footnotes are supplied by the translator.]

3

than in any other Romanian region.

Sublime longing, that special kind of longing which overwhelms you when - from the *calidor* - your sight blurred by sorrow, you look out towards the west, to where you think the Prut is, that accursed river which has divided us in two ever since the Muscovites took half of Moldavia from us and christened it: Bessarabia...

For far too short a time, and only at a few key moments was I actually standing on the place (and there you go, how could it have come down to us from the French, when they don't even have the essential verb *to stand*?), nevertheless I always return, incessantly and effortlessly, to exactly the same point of departure: the threshold of my life.

Of course art and literature - especially poetry - have painted, sung and consecrated another point-of-departure or view: the window. In prison I came to know it, visited it and, in my own way, celebrated it, but the *calidor*... The further I move away from it, my point-of-departure, the closer I move towards it, my point-of-arrival, and time is, like my journey, circular.

Like nearly all little boys I was, and remain, closer to my mother, because of the unsevered umbilical cord. Perhaps that is why the place I return to is not completely inside, as it is for the unborn, but it is a passage, an entrance open on both sides, outside, an outside which was proximal and not definitive, where there was air and light and shade and warmth, exposed to attacks - but not deadly ones; and whenever I liked, I could take the step backward to safety - a safety which was refused, for example, to Rilke in *Pietà*:

Now you're lying across my lap,
Now I can't give birth to you again...

Mother didn't send me: she guided me into the world; she didn't expel me, she led me by the hand. And when she left, when she withdrew, when she re-entered her own mother again, forever, as she let go of one of my hands, into my other hand she put another hand, the hand of my son

Filip (after thirteen years of agony, Mother's body had become smaller, her face retraced its steps along the path of evolution and acquired the features of a newborn; thirteen months later Filip arrived, like all newborn babies, with the face of an old woman - but not any old woman's face, Mother's face, as it was when she left us).

And so,...my hand,...to go out onto, and to come back in from the *calidor* of the house in Mana: the hub of the universe. The axis of the world.

The House

I said "my parents' house" although it wasn't my parents' property but belonged to the state, to the village in fact, as it was a wing of the school. Should I have said "the house in which I was born"? - that neither: I was born in the early hours of the morning of 2nd October 1935 "somewhere else", a good twenty metres nearer the back lane, in a mud hut covered with straw, which had been purchased along with the school grounds. And so, my parents' house didn't belong to my parents, and I wasn't born in it.

And yet because of *our house*, Father delayed seeking refuge west of the Prut following the 28th of June 1940, the awful day on which Basarabia and Bukovina were surrendered to the Russians. He kept delaying and putting things off - until it was too late.

"Why didn't we leave with the first lot of refugees, Dad, in 1940?" I asked him, when I was old enough to ask such a question. "Didn't you know what it was going to be like under occupation? Under the Bolsheviks?"

"We knew all there was to know, but it's one thing to know something from hearsay and another thing to live it for yourself. I knew quite a bit, not only from talking to the people who'd come over the Dniester, especially in the time of the famine in the Ukraine around '32 to '33, but also from what we hadn't forgotten ourselves. Where do you think the Russians started with that 'rivalution' of theirs?"

"In Petersburg - the cruiser *Aurora* - The Winter Palace - Stand up and fight! in our Caragiale's immortal words."

"And they fought, all right - if it had only been like that, I mean only in October...the bad bit was that when the

7

hullabaloo began - I'm talking about February now - part of their front was in Moldavia. When the Muscovites heard that it was all over for the boyars, the bourgies, the priests, the tsars and that *they* were going to get their hands on the land..."

"...They abandoned the trenches and left us to it, faced with the Germans and tens of miles of open front..."

"We say 'tens' because we're good-natured lads... But what was the point of putting them down there? So that Ivan from Tambov or Simbirsk could give up his life for Iasi or for Falticeni? But if it meant that when they left the front they could follow the trail back to Simbirsk and Tambov, to their boyars and bourgies...only they followed it back with...acts of justice in Moldavia which the people could have done without. And what they did to us in Basarabia...I was about eight or nine, I can remember it... Why do you think I'm not saying 'Up the revolution!'?"

"So you knew what the Bolsheviks were..."

"Bolsheviks! That word didn't frighten us - in fact it got the Wallachians off our backs - but when we heard about the collective farms...it seemed like one was giving birth to the next, but that's how we peasants look at things..."

"But you weren't a peasant any more, therefore you had no land to lose - or was that just why you stayed?"

"No, not because of that. And there weren't any 'therefores' either... Most of the peasants stayed where they were, even up to the second flight in '44."

"And then? Did you think you were badly off? I mean, look, you weren't too... - they pulled you in as well and sent you to Siberia..."

"If a Basarabian had the last traces of Romanian mentality...To the Occupation!", Father laughed. "Let's just say that I didn't leave with the first wave of refugees because of the house."

"Which house? We didn't have a house of our own!"

"What do you mean, we didn't have our own house?"

Father was getting annoyed. "What about the school? The school in Mana which I built with these hands?"

Ah yes, now I remembered. I mean, I could remember what they had all told me about it: Mother, Father, Old Iacob, Aunt Domnica...I was too young to register my own memories: four years and eight months old.

When the surrender was announced, Father said, "We're leaving!"

And Mother said, "Let's go then!"

And Old Iacob, our neighbour,

"Let's get goin' right now, who knows what t' expect from these old bones."

And Aunt Domnica, his wife,

"God be wi' you, an' take this parcel of food as well."

And Dodon the priest,

"Come with us, there's still room in the second cart - only don't bring your furniture."

And my father,

"Off you go, Father, don't let *your* furniture get wet. We'll catch you up, we have to get some things together..."

And to Mother, "Let's go, let's go, only a quick fly around the house and I'll go and find a carter. Only a quick whizz round and we're leaving..."

I was sitting on the *calidor* and I could *see*: I could see Father making only one more whizz around; and only one more and only one.... I could see Mother bringing all the suitcases, packages and bundles down into the courtyard. I could see Old Iacob helping her, in his own way, to bring the luggage down from the *calidor* into the yard: running about, one hand keeping his hat on his head, the other motioning this way and that:

"Just a second, just a second, I'm comin'...but can you manage, Missus?... Is it...?" he'd just arrived when Mother, who'd brought down one case or package, started going up the stairs again, and so he "arranged" what she'd just brought down, moving it two fingers to the left or to the right and saying to her from behind, "But can you manage somethin' like that? You're carryin' it by yerself! But this is man's work!"

Mother didn't even notice him, didn't see him or hear him, she knew the man in Old Iacob - who'd now taken off after Father and was making a quick whizz around the house with him, while Aunt Domnica was helping Mother just like her husband did - only she was doing so from inside the house.

"But you can't carry it alone, Missus, you might get a hernia!"

"That's man's work!" *she* said as well, while gripping our food parcel to her chest with both hands.

I was sitting on the *calidor* but couldn't see any more: night had fallen. But it wasn't so dark that I couldn't see:

Mother, dragging all the luggage in the opposite direction, from the courtyard, where the carter had unloaded it again, up the stairs and into the house. Aunt Domnica was trotting along beside her, with the parcel of food upside down but still clutched to her chest; Old Iacob was flying about trying to keep his hat on his head, while Mother had carried up all the cases and the packages, and then, after she'd been told that it was man's work, she went after the other man: Father. Father could now make his flying tours in peace: we weren't leaving any more. No, we did leave but we came back. No, we were turned back!

I was sitting on the *calidor* and I could hear the two men swirling and swilling the contents of a demijohn. I heard their voices:

"Ah, they's no great loss wi'out some small gain. To ev'ry cloud... He who laughs last..." (Old Iacob, heaving with laughter).

"Just as well they turned us back nearer to home - the poor horses, this way at least they only did forty kilometres round trip, imagine if they'd sent us back at the banks of the

10

Prut like they've done to so many others... How many kilometres is it to the Prut, Old Iacob?"

"Seventy, as th' crow flies, about a hundr'd by road - th' poor horses..."

"A hundred just to get there, and to come back? The poor horses (poor Father), we have to think of the horses as well..."

"Tha's right: th' horse, th' poor devil... Yaas. If you'd left yest'day... Last night, at least, or early in th' mornin'..."

"So we didn't leave when it was best to leave, but like you said, perhaps there's no great loss without some small gain..."

"It's up t' Him, God... Teacher-Sir, I know what it's like wi' the Russians, the Muscovites, they're people as well, good at heart, - only you've got t' know how t' handle 'em..."

"But these ones aren't Russians any more, Old Iacob, they've turned themselves into Soviets. They haven't got a God any more."

"Not so! Once a Russian always a Russian: scrape off a bit o' that Sovietic skin an' you'll find yer true orthodox believer underneath - I knooooow 'em, that's how I know 'em t' be, from the time o' the Muscovites... A Russian's like a sheep dog, you got t' know how t' handle 'im. Look, if you treat 'em easy, then... An' if God gives us a helpin' hand, well then..."

I didn't know whether God had given Old Iacob a helping hand, but I knew from my parents that it had always been easy for him; like when their commissary officers came to our village, how he went to greet them, with the traditional bread and salt:

"Welcome, comrades, they've sent me to tell you we've been lookin' forward to seein' you for aaaages! An' I'm not the mayor, y' know, only a kind of deputy, an' this Mana of ours is a tiny village, not a commune - an' that's in the first place; secondly, y' should know I'm not a deputy 'cause I wanted t' be, the Romanians forced me - an' if I didn't

11

they'd've thrown me in jail as a *borshevik*; an' thirdly I'm a poor peasant, I've got nothin' but a little house an' a little patch o' vines - for makin' meself a drop - but I give it all t' th' collective farm, we hand it over wi' love; an' fourthly, I've never had a servant, was a servant meself for the boyars, 'til I was freed by the Great Rivalution - th' whole village is my witness and th' villages round about - that's my lot!"

Talking about the "welcome", Mother pursed her mouth and said something. I couldn't make it out, but it wasn't good; Father took to Old Iacob's defence:

"What could he do, poor man? And he wasn't really lying: he was a servant in the time of the Russians; he didn't have anything apart from the house and the vineyard; he didn't get on with the Romanian administration, he used to say that Greater Romania, instead of sending us 'luminaries', sent us 'convicts' - he said:

" 'Huh, now that Romania's a great country, wi' colonies an' its own Siberia, they send us all sorts o' robbers an' idlers who've been caught wi' the goods in Wallachia. Look at 'em, Teacher-Sir! only at what we sees here in th' villages: where's th' teachers? gendarmes? civil servants? We get th' scum o' Wallachia! That joke o' theirs is no accident -*send 'em to Romanian Siberia!* Instead of lockin' 'em away there, in jail as bad people, they send 'em to us, as good people! Look at the way they come: barefoot, hardly a rag on their backs, their worldly goods in a straw bag - a rush basket, as they calls it; in a month, they're wearin' clothes an' shoes, in three they're marryin' so-and-so's daughter, in six they bring one of th' brothers up from Wallachia, in nine months this brother brings a cousin an' a sister-in-law, within a year th' whole family's moved in; in two years they're goin' round in a gig, in three years, a automobile, 'cause they've got their hand on so-and-so's mill, so-and-so's oil press, th' vineyards over this way, th' houses over that way, shops, the lot - worse than th' Jews!' "

"He was exaggerating, of course," I said.

"Of course, but not a lot...It's true, after the Great War, Romania didn't have enough 'luminaries' to go round - she'd buried her flowers at Marasesti, Oituz and Casin - but it's also true that Basarabia was 'helped', mostly with newcomers and jailbirds - like in the colonies, as Old Iacob used to say. Perhaps that's one of the reasons why, when you looked into many of the houses, between the icons was a portrait of the tsar..."

"Old Iacob had one as well, but he got sick of it during the Occupation of '40-'41. But let's get back to what we were talking about. Why didn't we leave on time, to seek refuge? You said it was because of the house and the school; but you weren't the only teacher in Basarabia to have built the village school with your own hands."

"No," said Father. "Many built bigger and better ones. Those people also had something other than the school, something of their own: a house, land..."

"...and better reasons for not leaving: things to lose."

"Is that what you think?" Father sighed. "They say that you miss the little things more than the big ones. When you've got a lot to lose, you can afford...to lose."

The first time I heard this reasoning I didn't understand it; and Father didn't go out of his way to explain it to me, so I made merciless fun of it. I got an inkling of the meaning in later years, when I heard that a poetess, newly arrived in Paris, had declared she would rather die of hunger than work with her hands... "All well and good, dear girl," Mrs X had said, "But in the first years of exile even Mrs So-and-so worked as a hospital orderly, Miss So-and-so was a salesgirl - as for me, I was a cleaning lady for years... And my...'escutcheon' hasn't come crashing down..." To which the Poetess had replied: "Of course not...yours can't fall..." Mrs X asked her to explain. The Poetess: "It's very simple, Mrs Y and Miss X and yourself, Madam, are ladies, *you* can afford to become servants; but I am a peasant, Madam, *I* cannot afford to..."

13

The School

The fact is, Father had only just started out. He, too, could not afford to.

The school he had continued to dance rings around until he'd left it too late, was that little something that was too little to part company with; that little thing he made with his own hands and not just by making "sacrifices", as they say; but with one supreme sacrifice: a young lad quarrying stone to use in the foundations had been crushed to death in a landslide.

Although Pantelimon Severin - that was the boy's name - had already passed the age of seventeen, due to the repeated (and enthusiastic) interventions of my father, the age limit had been waived and he was granted permission to attend the teacher training school in Orhei. It went without saying: after finishing his studies, he would return to Mana - therefore, he had been working for his school from its very inception: clearing the land (including the mud hut I was born in...), digging the foundations, making "cooking shells" for the bricks to dry in. And the stone he took was from the slope of a nearby hill... Feeling guilty about the boy's death - hadn't he been the one to put the idea of being a teacher into his head? - Father stopped work on the site and requested a transfer (after his resignation was refused). However, the people from the village, led by Pantelimon's parents, persuaded him to stay and carry on with the work because, as they said: "Foundations should be built with souls" - so they buried the young lad observing tradition, and on the fourth day even more people turned up to work "at the school".

After the unhappy event, Father addressed reports and

written requests to the Inspectorate in the name of the villagers, asking for their approval to call the primary school in Mana *Pantelimon Severin*. He received the reply, "We find the proposal lacking in any foundation, since we have no evidence of the person of the same name distinguishing himself in the enlightenment of the people." However, the people of Mana had their own opinions about those who had (or had not) distinguished themselves; about foundation and foundations; and, without applying or waiting for approval from above, they started saying that they were "goin' to work at Pantelimon", or that so-and-so lives "in th' second house on th' left, after Pantelimon". And from there, it was only a small step to the designation of *Pantelimon* for the school as an institution; then as a course in reading and writing; then as the certificate received - all bore...the name of *the person-of-the-same-name*. Thus, the children "went to *Pantelimon*"; so-and-so had "fourth level *Pantelimon*" - while Pantelimon's wife could hardly sign her name. The pupils themselves became *Pantelimons* about seven years after the unfortunate event, not only because they attended *Pantelimon* but also because about three-quarters of the boys born after the death of "the person" were so christened, Pantelimon (not to mention the girls, Pantelimona...). Mother claimed that when I was born, she had fought with my father for a long time to stop me being christened Pantelimon as well. Father, however, denied it and said that it wasn't him but the village people who really would have liked "Teacher-Sir's" boy to be called Pantelimon, to be even more a part of them.

I'm standing on the *calidor* and I can see...I can see something I've never seen before, not even in photographs: the house where I was born.

"It wasn't even a mud hut when we arrived," Father said. "At some stage, a long time before, it had served as somewhere to live, but then it was just a ruin: the neighbours dumped their rubbish there, passers-by did their business there. The elder bushes, and even the weeds, had overgrown it. When we came to Mana, we rented a room at Severin's, Pantelimon's father. During the day we used it as a classroom and at night, we lived there. Under the Russians, the village didn't have four walls you could call a school, the church buildings were also in ruins - later, Dodon was appointed priest and he repaired them, for his own use...In the mornings, I gave classes and at lunchtime I set off on a horse I'd hired to ask for people's help: to Orhei, to the Inspectorate, to the monasteries, to the landowners, what was left of them - there were still a few, but they lived in Chisinau, Bucharest or in Paris. The state gave us a plot of land and a lot of pupils. Well, it turned out that the labour involved in building the school was to be 'voluntary' - but what about the materials? If it had been up to me, my man, the school would have been a solid building, made of brick, on stone foundations, with a tiled or slate roof. Considering the size of the village, at least two classrooms, an office and staffroom, a room for a museum, another one for a library, an assembly room which, on the days we had classes, could also serve as a canteen - I thought it wouldn't be a bad idea if the pupils had their lunch and a snack there, a few at a time... I mean a school, my man, a real school!"

Old Iacob had said:

"All well an' good, Teacher-Sir, but if you want everythin' from the beginnin', in the end you're left wi' nothin'. Brick, y'say, but where are you goin' to get brick from? You'd have to bring it from Orhei and you'd pay through the nose for it; you want tiles - where are you goin' to get tiles - Orhei again, you'd pay through the nose for them - an' we won't even talk about slate. When a man wants t' make himself a house, he has a look round and does a bit of reck'nin' and makes it out of what's there, on th' spot, not wi' nonsense from the town!"

"I had a look around and did a bit of reckoning," Father said. "Do you want me to make the school out of shell

16

moulds for the bricks? To make the roof out of reeds? Plaster them down with dung? So it doesn't look any different from people's houses? The *school*?"

"But why sh'd it look any diff'rent?" asked Old Iacob. "You want it t' be diff'rent from the rest?"

"Well of course it'll be different because it'll last for ten years, not five, when it'll look like that!" - and Father pointed to the ruin in the back lane, on the land which had been purchased for the school. "How do you expect these things to last, if you make them out of clay and reeds?"

Father never saw the brighter side of it, because, in the end, he had to build the school not out of stones, nor out of bricks, but out of the "cooking shells" for bricks; and he had to make the roof out of reeds. I have a confession to make: out of inherited embarrassment, until just a few years ago I used to avoid showing photographs of myself at the age of one, or three... Because behind us, in the photograph, was "the house" - the school that is - and if you couldn't tell that the walls were made of "cooking shells", it was obvious that the roof was made out of reeds...

On one occasion, towards the end of an interview I was giving to a German magazine (the team also included a photographer who took photographs...of the family photos), a Franco-Italian friend visited me. He's a writer, publicity agent, and an architect as well... He looked through the photographs and...deeply offended me: instead of noting my august presence (I was, after all, in the centre, between Mother and Father), he raved about...the background! About the house with the roof made of reeds!

Peeved, I wondered about this: how was it that *he*, in the first place a Frenchman, and in the second an architect (and an Italian...) could go into ecstasies about a hovel made out of clay and covered with reeds? Out of politeness? Out of a taste for the exotic, for the unusual? He should go to the Loire, and have a look at what the Gallo-Roman troglodytes did!

What was I talking about? he replied, laughing. On the contrary, he had been knocked over by the equilibrium of the construction, the harmony, the good taste, the...compatibility of the materials... What materials: you could see the reeds, but the brick "cooking shells"? They were covered in mud and the dust of whitewash - *and* the dust of forty years since the photograph had been taken... My friend, however, continued to extol their virtues, stopping only from time to time to ask for technical details: how were these "cooking shells" made...what did I call them in Romanian, *cochileti*? Interesting, it doesn't come from *coquille* by any chance, from the shape of them? What, they don't just put straw in the clay, but tow as well? Interesting, like the base for fresco - ah, it's not a local custom, was it your father's idea then? Excellent! I see, first the skeleton is made with wooden reinforcements? Why? Surely the shells are strong enough to support one floor, especially since the roof is so light? Ah, I see, the region's ravaged by earthquakes, that explains it, the horizontal beams are oak and the vertical ones acacia - or was it the other way round? - aaah, acacia isn't subject to torsion...

I hadn't a clue whether Father had put tow into the clay or not, or whether the vertical beams were acacia (as opposed to the horizontal oak ones...), and when it comes down to it I hadn't the faintest idea if there even was a wooden "skeleton"... How to God was I supposed to know how the brick shells were laid, even if I'd seen them, I couldn't have remembered bits and bobs, the inferiority complex which Father had inculcated in me (like every peasant, he would have preferred it if his rise up the social scale had been accompanied, naturally, by a rise up the scale of materials from which he was to build his house) would have compelled me to forget. And yet: rather than give the impression that I didn't know (and I did not) I began to...well, yes, to build, *to make* (with my own hands) "my" house. And it's so easy, you get a lot of pleasure out of building a house for yourself. It was all the easier, and more pleasurable (even technically speaking) because it was...or more precisely it would have been, the first. Even if I'd ever had another house, or even several houses; or if I'd really built them with my own hands; or if I'd been a builder by trade - I still wouldn't have been able to build the house with more know-how, or more pleasure - when words failed me, I resorted to pencil and paper, drawing one "detail" or another - and even the odd "secret" (of construction, of course...). My friend listened and watched, his mouth opening wider and wider; he asked me to go over certain points and to give him more details. Suddenly he said, "You never told me you were an architect as well."

I danced my way out of it, "And even worse: I'm a writer..." - and so the game went well...for me, because I also had a sense of humour (!) and I was, as far as he was concerned, "in the brotherhood"; for him because - probably - he was sharing a secret with me, all the more worth keeping because I had let him in on it, without actually letting him in on anything... However, our complicity was cut short. When he pointed to my drawings and asked me, "Are all the houses in Basarabia built like this?" I replied quite sharply, huffed with it all: "NO!" What got into me to put the matter straight, I don't know - I started to tell him the truth, that everything I had told him and had drawn was...out of a novel. He didn't believe me. And then *he* went into a huff: was I trying to take my toys back from him?

I'm sitting on the *calidor* of the house in Mana. I'm looking at the space between the outside gate and the little inside gate, it's now as smooth as the palm of your hand, polished, like the schoolyard it now is. I know (now) that that was where the ruin was, which Father wouldn't even call a mud hut; I know now that the ruin, repaired at random (I suppose the major priority was the roof) is where my brother, little Peter, was born and where he died; and I know that it's also the place where I was born.

From where I am now, today, I'm still looking out from the *calidor*. And I'm saying to myself that I'd like to be able to say "Look, I was born here" - and to point to something that was still standing, a crumbling wall, part of the chimney worn away and swept by time - and not just to point to the flat ground with an indecisive gesture meaning, "somewhere around here..." Today, nearly fifty years later, if not even the schoolhouse is there any more, the one Father built with his own hands - it's not important: it will still stand (and if it falls down, we'll build an even-bigger-and-better-one) solid in my own memories, memories born out of the memories of my parents and from photographs. What I do miss now is something that was already missing before I was capable of registering a memory: a static visual image - I have to resort to a vague, rather circular gesture, excruciatingly expansive in its hesitancy, and to the words "somewhere around here..."

Those people who were born there before and after me (but who stayed exactly where they were) won't have felt the same lack yet, they'll be used to moving about, but staying within the heart of it all. I, however, left the little circle a long time ago and once and for all, and the threshold I always return to is perhaps not even a metre and a half higher than the ground in the schoolyard.

But it's suspended...

"Listen," Father said, as he had said to Old Iacob: "How do you expect the things you make to last, if you make them out of clay and reeds?"

To which the Old Iacob in me could reply - if *he* hadn't done so himself:

"A house's like a man, Teacher-Sir: earth-to-earth..."

As it was in the beginning, is now and ever shall be: a house is like a man, it returns to the earth from which it came.

But if it is like that - and it should be - then everything

can be explained, all the wounds can be healed, all the injustices put to right. Which is what I tried to do with my Franco-Italian friend - and architect to boot.

I didn't succeed with my friend - not that I tried. What should I have explained to him? Should I have tried to express in drawing my verbal explanation? I, a writer? Although he was a writer as well, he wouldn't have understood how I, with my own hands, could build a house, on the model of the pretzel - by rolling the dough into a given hole. I'm rolling words into the threshold. Thresh-old, be-bold, into the mould...

The Village

"When your mother wrote the monograph on Mana, she went back to... Let's see what you know, how far back, who did she start with?"

"She went back to the 'Inevitable' Stephen", I said. "You can't have a conversation with a Basarabian that lasts more than two sentences before he tells you that he is 'one of Stephen's peasants, by bond...', which gives you the impression that both the settlements and especially the people only starting walking on two legs in the 15th century - if not even later..."

"As far as 'the Inevitable Stephen' is concerned, we'll settle that score another time," Father said. "And as for the bonds the Basarabians are always flattering themselves about, if you knew the history behind it - but you don't. That's how we Romanians are: when we haven't really got a lot of history, and in fact we've only got a little, we still don't know it well. You'll find, little scribe, that with these bonds the 'Inevitable' only confirmed a situation, a state of affairs which had been going on from the time of his - and his peasants' - ancient ancestors. But we were talking about Mana. The village existed - by name at least - from the time of Peter I..."

"Over a hundred, hundred-and-fifty years, then?"

"I'm not talking about Peter of Russia, the Tsar, confound him - because of him, the Turks brought us to our knees once and for all and imposed Phanariot rule* on us, because of him, Peter - *the Great* for the Russians - he

---

* *Phanariot rule* - Greeks from the Phanar district of Constantinople, hence Phanariots, were appointed princes of the Romanian principalities (Moldavia and Wallachia) by the Turks under whose auspices they ruled. The Phanariot period lasted from 1711 to 1821.

brought only ruin to our country..."

"Take it easy, take it easy, old man! If you think about history in terms of *because of*, you'll end up back with Cain, if not with Eve. And don't forget that our blood's got a bit of *phana*..."

"You, not me! You're greco... Look, let's move on... I was talking about Peter I, prince of Moldavia before Alexander the Good - they used to call him 'The Camomile Child', he ruled between 1375 and 1391; Peter, father of Roman, 'prince of all Moldavia...up to the sea...' "

"Let's forget about Roman-prince-up-to-the-sea for a while and get back to his father: is he by any chance the one and the same Peter who surrendered Moldavia to the Poles?"

Father is a teacher who knows his history. I am his son, I am not a teacher, the teacher is my father - and so he lost his temper:

"Sur-ren-dered! It was the thing of the moment, a fashion, every country, no matter how great-and-strong, surrendered to another which was even greater and even stronger. To surrender was like saying hello - look, even today the Transylvanians greet each other with *Servus!* That is, 'I'm your slave...' "

"Don't get excited, I was talking about political surren-der."

"Political surrender! And you... If we take it that way then even Stephen the Great surrendered..."

"And how! It was such a ... thing of the moment, that from then onwards Moldavia didn't have a window over the Danube and the sea..."

"Yes, my man; that-that-that Stephen of ours, the Great and the Saintly, has got a lot to answer for. It's difficult not to cry over spilt milk, but between us men - can I tell that story, in class, to young children? Me, a Basarabian, to stand and say that Chilia and Cetatea Alba were lost by that great Stephen of ours?"

23

"The children are Transylvanians now, you can say anything nasty you like about the Moldavians..."

"He surrendered, he surrendered, he followed fashion - to the Poles and to the Hungarians and to the Turks - but didn't he give them all a hiding as well? True, one of them at a time, with the help of the others... Yes, my man, His-to-ry has a lot to answer for. If that was our lot: let's give in little-by-little, let's surrender again - so we don't perish,...destroyed, swallowed up by our beloved neighbours... And listen, they did perish, they came to ruin: the Tartars and the Turks have gone, Poland and Hungary have got smaller, shrunk, a fine state they're in... Only Russia is spreading out, always spreading - like ringworm; only our brothers, Christian and Orthodox, the Russians, haven't given us a very easy time..."

Not really, no. Not at all, in fact.

The fate of our village is exemplary: mentioned in documents from as far back as the second half of the 14th century (and then as a gift to a monastery, thus it had been a village even before then), Mana had survived, always built itself up again from the ashes of the fires, the pillaging, the passing through of all the "passers-by": Tartars, Poles, Lithuanians, Swedes, Turks, Cossacks, Russians... But what the fires and the swords of the aggressors hadn't succeeded in doing, what the Russian army didn't manage to do (the one which said that it was setting out on a Holy War against the Pagans, until Tarigrad [Constantinople] was liberated, the army that settled, forcibly, in Romanian lands - her friends, it said - and which kept forgetting to go back home - a year, seven years, twenty years...), the administration, after the 1812 occupation of "Bessarabia", concluded perfectly.

As a reward for who-knows-what great merits, an Italian (he could have been German or French because, in the last analysis, who made Russia great? The Germans: army, administration, industry; the French: diplomacy, and even if only that, wasn't that enough? the Italians: brick upon brick, starting with the Kremlin in Moscow, sweeping through the whole of Petersburg, to Odessa - which was conceived by the French...), and so, this deserving man (who, as it happened was Italian) received an estate. However, since the large properties in this newly occupied land belonged to the monasteries (being Orthodox, they were hesitant about giving them to any Catholic), and since the Moldavian peasants of our area didn't know serfdom - not even the word - they knew themselves, as far back as anybody knows, as freeholding peasants - the Italian was given the gift of a village: Mana. He was given "in everlasting service, to him and to his descendants" not only the land (property, hayfields, vineyards, pastures, forests, grazing land); not only, let's say, "the land under the houses" - but, following the Russian custom (hadn't this half of Moldavia become by then a Russian province, baptised "Bessarabia", a spelling supplied by French cartographers...?), also "the souls". A nice way of putting it: *souls* - which only goes to prove, if there was any need, the good-soul of the Russian, his Slav charm... Slaves, servants, men were turned into cattle or tools, and those convertible into money were lost in card games. These people were not what they really were: serfs and slaves, but...in Christian, Russian words, *souls*. When the Moldavian peasants found out that, by a stroke of the pen, the Russians had stolen not only their possessions but also their freedom - even though they had replaced them with the title of *soul* - in the course of a single night, a good thousand of... *souls* disappeared.

Where? Ah, but no, they hadn't ascended into heaven. Where? Anywhere. Or: right in front of your eyes. The majority of the inhabitants fled to the west, over the river Prut into the half of Moldavia which was still free, still not transformed into imperial "gifts", villages in which the people were still people, still non-*souls*, bestowed by the new masters, the Russians, on new-Russians in particular - who we must admit *had* toiled, and to top it all, with faith! -

toward the building of Great Russia.

Once they were abandoned, the reed-covered mud houses were blown down by the winds, eroded by the rains; ruined and fallen, they became one with the earth from which they were made. In place of the villagers of Mana - savages who hadn't yet grasped the "higher stage of civilisation" (as the historians write today), they brought civilisers from the civilised depths of Russia, *souls*-as-far-back-as-anybody-knows, *souls*-from-father-to-son; then came freed convicts; then Muscovites, veterans who had finished their twenty-year military service; and finally wanderers who had been free peasants and had fled from their villages, thrown out or expelled from their land in the South, around the Danube delta and the coast, where the Russians had cleaned up the area and installed huge colonies of German, Swiss and French people, some survivors from the Grande Armée - who were colonised in newly-named villages, names which sounded sweet to Gallo-Napoleonic ears: Berezina, Borodino, Arcis (-*sur-Aube*)...

The Italian's first accomplishment (the people called him the *'Talian* or, for onomastic revenge, *Sirdar Ali* and *Sir Ali*) was the building of "The Court". However, before it was finished, "God gave us 'n earthquake", as Old Iacob used to say. This rendered "The Palace of the *Sirdar*" into a heap of yellowish-pink stones.

The second accomplishment of the *'Talian Sir Ali*: he forbade his *souls* to repair and make their homes in the houses which had been abandoned by non-*souls*. He might have been Italian on his mother's side, but by Mother Russia, who'd made him what he was, he was Russian: he gave the order that the old village dwellings were to be abandoned and that the *souls* were to be installed in the immediate proximity of the Court (still under reconstruction). Not, however, in *houses* - only natives lived in houses above the ground...*souls* had to shelter in pit-houses... And only in pit-houses (as was the custom...).

His third accomplishment was also his last: he started teaching the servants of the Court the *Pater Noster* - in Latin, of course. The unforgivable Papist heresy reached the very souls of the Orthodox believers. And thus, it's said, *Sirdar Ali* (perhaps he was called Sardelli?) disappeared as master from the wilds of Mana. In his place appeared (word has it that only his name appeared, the man himself never set foot on the estate) another "Great Russian", as Old Iacob used to say, who also said he must have been called Wolfgang Ludwigovici or Guido Cezarevici, if not Jeanjacquovici Dupontov...

Thus after 1918, when "Bessarabia" became Basarabia, Mana was a kind of new village, and there were scores of them in the colonised South, although you could count them on the fingers of one hand in the forests and in the Upper Country (that is, in the central and northern areas of Moldavia). The inhabitants of Mana: ex-*souls*, slaves brought from Russia, ex-wanderers who had been rounded up and forced to settle there. What intrigued Mother was: although the majority were of Russian origin, the villagers of Mana couldn't speak Russian. They blubbered a few words or expressions they'd picked up in the army or town - however, in a Romanianized form - and no more than the Romanians had. And, with four or five exceptions (among whom were Old Iacob and Severin), they were illiterate. Mother used to say, "profoundly illiterate..."

Between the Union of 1918 and the time in which my parents arrived as teachers in Mana, many things had changed for the good - in the province of Basarabia, in the towns, in the other villages - however nothing, absolutely nothing in Mana. Bit-by-bit the estate of the last "Great Russian" had been expropriated, and the Mana villagers had also received land ("from Averescu", they laughed, as if the General himself had handed it to them, along with a handshake) - to what end? The people were no longer *souls*, they had gained their freedom and land, however...

"Well, Ion," Father told me he'd said, in his first years as an apostle in Mana, "you received five hectares of fine arable land from the Reform - why are you fooling around, why don't you work the land?"

"What d'you mean, I'm not workin' it, Teacher-Sir?" Father said that this Ion had replied. "I've sown one length wi' wheat, another wi' corn - an' what's left, I've put watermelons down..."

"That's so, you've done that - but what about the two hectares you've left fallow?"

"They're restin', poor hectares that they are...for th' land's like man an' th' Lord, it works as hard as it can, but on th' seventh day it puts everythin' down, to get its breath back... Don't worry, Teacher-Sir, 'cause next year I'll put somethin' down over that way an' this bit here'll have a rest - for th' land's like th' Lord an' man..."

"That's true," Father said he'd said. "Like man, like field - I saw how you sowed the wheat: you scratched the soil a little bit, so as not to hurt it too much - your kind of sowing, with furrows waving this way and that...I've never seen the like! You threw the seeds over your shoulder, made the sign of the cross: Lord, bring the rain! and then you sat straight down on the porch of your house!"

"On th' porch - but where's I suppos'd t' sit?"

"But you're not supposed to sit! Get out into the fields!"

"Why sh'd I go to th' fields now, Teacher-Sir? T' pull the wheat up by th' leaves an' make it grow? If th' Lord gives us a bit o' rain, an' He doesn't send us hail, then in two-three years' time th' wheat'll grow right up t' Him, Teacher-Sir, an' th' fenugreek up t' your chin!"

"For the moment, only the horse-thistles are growing, tall enough to poke your eyes out! Go out and do some weeding!"

"But why sh'd I go? Weeds 're th' grass o' th' Devil, what I pulls out just grows more quickly. I did some weedin', like

28

y'say, at th' beginnin', after th' Reform, but what's th' use? I pulls one out in front o' me, takes a step forward, an' it's already grown back behind me, up over me ankles - I swear it, Teacher-Sir! Leave it, leave it, th' thresher's comin'. That machine works like in th' Scriptures: *And the wheat'll be sorted from the chaaaaaff,*" Ion sang; he sang and laughed, in the shade of his porch...

So Father told me, laughing strangely enough himself...

I don't know who this Ion was, but I know he could've been anybody - apart from Old Iacob (who never ever worked) and from Severin - who was a "newcomer", that's to say he came to Mana from his own village, a freehold village, after 1918, to get even more land. "He was like a machine", according to some; while to others, "he may toil like an idiot, but he won't get more than we do in the next world..."

"In any case, this Ion used the rotation system," I said.

"He used...the 'let's-wait-ation' system, as the Wallachians say now. The Reform was fine, but the land was given to devils and men. The land was fine, but what could you work it with? Even real peasants didn't have animals to pull the ploughs with any more, to say nothing of the villagers of Mana... The horses had been requisitioned, all of them, from '14 onward, for the Russian front in Galitia. The oxen, they'd been eaten by the army... I didn't see this myself, but Old Iacob told me: Severin reined himself up with his wife, and they shoved their own necks in the yoke and pulled... That's how Severin ploughed and harrowed - but how can you ask a *soul* to put himself in the yoke of his own accord? Only a free man, a free pleasant like Severin, could do it of his own accord..."

"In any case, this Ion fellow put watermelons down as well," I said. "If nothing was yielded from the wheat and the corn, he could have made some money from the melons..."

"Huh, to make money!... The Manians didn't put down melons to sell them - who'd buy? There were some Jews who were in it wholesale; they supplied Mana as well...melons were all you could think about... To eat them? - a few basketfuls would've been enough, not hectares..."

"And so why did they put melons down?"

"Why? So that they could move their backsides from the porch to the watchtowers to look after the melons!"

"I remember them. The nicest one was Morcov's..."

"What was left of it... You didn't see their best times. After the Occupation, whether they kept growing melons or not, their watchtowers were sure to be so..."

"...tall - in her monograph on Mana, Mother drew some of them and noted the dimensions. Was it true Blanaru's was over 20 metres high?

"I don't think your mother wrote 20 metres, we measured them together. They were all about 10 metres."

"Mother told me that the first time, when you went to Mana..."

"The first time? I'll tell you what it was like: we came along the highroad - me pedalling, she sitting on the frame..."

"Wait a minute," Mother interrupted. "Take it from the beginning, nobody rushes you over memories."

"Where from, then?" laughed Father. "From the ball?"

"No, forget the ball, take it from the Inspectorate: we go to Orhei and ask them to give us the most difficult village..."

"The most difficult school," Father corrected. "So, we asked: Give us the biggest and most difficult school - up till then, the pair of us had been doing our two years of probationary teaching, we'd just got married..."

"Wait, dear, you've forgotten the ball!"

"But you said miss it out..."

"All right, miss it out...Lord, how we used to dance: we started at four in the afternoon, and the next morning at eight o'clock we were still dancing - without music, the musicians left at about three, they couldn't go on any longer..."

"They didn't leave, they ran away!" Father laughed.

"Your mother was the terror of the band; within a radius of fifty kilometres, when you hired a dance-band, before they'd tell you the price, the leader would ask: 'By any chance is Miss Popescu coming, Holban from Chistelinita's daughter? In that case, get yourself another group, look what she did to us last Sunday...' and they'd point to their swollen lips..."

"You're exaggerating, old man..." Mother protested, her eyes misty with pleasure. "I didn't do anything to them..."

"You didn't! You danced even in the intervals, to no music, they couldn't rest, the poor men..."

"Let's move on to the Inspectorate, when we asked for the most difficult school - you tell the story, go on."

"And the Inspector said, 'Because you are good and, in particular, courageous people, I'm giving you, not the most difficult school, but the most difficult village: Mana.' He went on, 'I'm giving it to you, so when you get frightened, you haven't got far to run till you reach me, only ten kilometres...' "

"That's what the Inspector said; but perhaps it wouldn't be a bad idea to tell the boy about my last ball as a Miss, the one at Scorteni, when you put the kerchief on my head and made me say Yes, instead of me staying single for another two or even five years and being able to dance, to dance... Lord, how inspired You were on the seventh day, when You danced!"

Mother danced and danced until illness confined her to bed. Later on, when she discovered the name of the illness (sclerosis of the platelets), even after she found out that there was no cure, she would say:

"If something had to grab hold of me anyway, I wish it had seized me by the hands and left my legs alone, so that I could..."; and she'd stop there, look around, shrug her shoulders and add, "so that I could walk..."

However, she would look at us with a translucence in her eyes and we knew what she really meant to say.

I still remember her dancing at the village balls - most

31

often with Father and most especially the waltz. Both of them were good dancers, but they danced even better together, so it's not surprising that they decided to marry during a ball. I find it more difficult to remember her dancing to music with light shoes on than I do remembering her heavy boots or waterproofs, moving around the floor in rhythm, in front of the oven, or under the table when she was sitting down; and also the rounded "starting off" movement she would make, for example when going from one place to another in the house to fetch something, like a jar from a cupboard; and also her eyes - at that moment they weren't on her face, but were in her dancing boots and wellies. It was not important, or of little importance, if she was listening to music on the radio at the time; she had her own band which played on in our intervals.

She told me the story, with her usual amused and intrigued expression, about the state security police, the Securitate, at Medias in Transylvania, when the women were held "in the kitchen". (My parents were arrested in January 1949, only a few weeks after the Securitate was founded. The new service had just installed itself in a house belonging to an industrialist; there were no cells, men were "in the garage", women, "in the kitchen", those punished and still alive, "in the cellar".) And so, one day the Commandant himself, the terrible Major Buzescu, came down into the kitchen and started shouting at Mother in particular, accusing her that....*she was ruining the bitch*, and threatening her that if she kept on doing that bourgeois, corrupt dance they call the waltz, he'd break her legs with his own hands.

I asked her what it meant, "ruining the bitch"? What bitch?

What do you mean, what bitch? The famous Lady of Medias, the whole of Transylvania knew about her: a female wolf-hound trained to bite the "villain" who either let his hands drop or otherwise interrupted the *manège* of questioning. "Upstairs" (during interrogation), Lady had guarded

32

my villain of a mother, once when she had her hands above her head for several hours and another time in the "Holy Virgin" (the name Buzescu gave to the position in which the victim had to keep his fingertips pressed to the tips of his toes - but keep his legs perfectly straight).

When she was transferred back to the kitchen, Mother came across Lady again - the famous dog rested there in between work sessions. The women didn't dare to move or speak - the animal had been with all of them "upstairs". Neither did Mother - out of fear. However, although she remained standing "as regulation required", Mother...was dancing: with her eyes, her head, and shifting her feet on the floor. After a short time, the bitch started to move as well, balancing her head from side to side as she watched Mother. It became obvious that Lady had developed a taste for the dance, not only when she was resting in the kitchen, but probably upstairs as well, during the interrogations, why else would the Commandant have become so incensed? It would appear that Lady was thoroughly ruined; she was no longer brought out "to deal with things", as they would say - and not because there weren't enough "villains" to keep guard over (alas, the spring-summer of 1949...).

After the first attack of her illness, Mother couldn't walk any more, or only with two sticks, pitiably trying to recover her legs as if from the dead. I put a chaise longue out on the grass in the courtyard. Because she always felt the cold in her legs (she had about fifty words and a hundred expressions to describe the different degrees of pain), she put several layers of stockings on - made of cotton, wool, and later, leggings made of rabbit or lamb skin. And we had to buy her men's felt slippers, size 41, overshoes which she called "cripple-overs". Sometimes, when she thought no one could see her, the cripple-overs started to move on the grass. In fact, they moved only a centimetre or two; their success was due to the efforts of Mother's shoulders. At the beginning the cripple-overs wouldn't listen to any orders;

however, little-by-little, following the example of her shoulders, there was a transfer: the cripple-overs only had to stay where they were on the grass, shapeless and weak, and in their place up above, the shoulders danced...and Mother's head and expression - of course, only and always the waltz, waltz, waltz...

"...That's what the Inspector said: 'When you get frightened, you've got only ten kilometres to run!' Your mother pulled me to one side and whispered: 'Let's not tell him we're getting married, he'll feel obliged to give us a wedding present...' I said, 'Perhaps you're right.' He was my teacher for pedagogy, and I was his best student... Your mother said to him, 'If you say the village is so near, we'll nip along there now - and see how bad it is.' 'Fine, off you go. When you return come and see me; if it's too late for the office, come over to my house. You know where it is, Goma...' "

And so, I'm sitting on the *calidor* and I can see a bicycle coming closer on the main road from Orhei: Father at the pedals, Mother sitting over the frame on an embroidered cushion. Granted, Father didn't actually steal Mother away. (My grandparents in Chistelnita weren't against the marriage; however, they did say the girl was right when she said it was too early, and it would be a good idea to stay single for one or two more years, to enjoy being a girl - dancing, dancing...) But did he whistle to her from the gate one night? He whistled to her. And did Mother come out, by the window, barefoot, with shoes in one hand and a shawl in the other? She came out. And when Father said, "I've come to take you, *get on!*" what did Mother do? *She got on!* True, not onto a Murg, or a Tintat or a Balan - but onto an Adler...

Come to think of it, when the night air smells of dried hay dampened by the dew and of goosefoot and of nightshade, can an eloping girl really differentiate between the shaking of a horse's back (with a green saddle) and that of a bicycle frame (with an arched saddle - again, for young men, not for girls...)? All the less so, since the shawl she had run away with contained an embroidered cushion, especially made for putting on the back of a frame, so it wouldn't break... And even more to the point, the mother of the girl not only heard, but saw from the window through the darkness (like any new mother-in-law), exactly what was happening in her house and courtyard, and so gave her husband (who was smoking beside her) a tap on the hand:

"Things are getting bad for the girls of today if they have to elope on a bi-cy-cle... What do you think, Toader? "

"What am I supposed to think?" said Toader. "Only that they have good luck on the way and that a horse-thistle doesn't get into one of Goma's tyres, so they have to start again and elope tomorrow night - I think there's rain coming..."

"No, Toader!" Grandmother said. "I'm not asking you about them, I'm asking you about us..."

· "In that case, we did it how it was done in our day: on a horse."

"When that boy comes round here again, I'm going to get him to give me a little ride on a bi-cy-cle, to see what's better to elope on," said Grandmother.

(In my day, the best thing to elope with was a tractor.)

"...We'd come to Orhei from Chistelnita on the bicycle," Father continued, "forty kilometres, not counting the ten to Mana - the main road was good, paved... We were getting closer to the village, you could see the church steeple... Your mother asked me to stop, to see something - but when you're struggling with the pedals, with somebody sitting on the frame, even if it is your lovely little bride, you're not dying to contemplate the countryside... I stopped - and what could we see? On our left, between the main road and the edge of the forest about a kilometre away: melon towers. We've got them in our area, at Ciocalteni as well. They also serve as shelters from the rain there, or as watchtowers too:

three or four strong poles, a platform, a roof made of reeds, a ladder - because watermelons are cultivated 'like reptiles', you watch over them from above, and from a tower three metres high you can also see for at least a kilometre - but here... Your mother said, 'The Inspector was lying to us, you know, about the difficult village, look, he's given us a wedding present.' I said, 'Going by the melon towers, Mana isn't a difficult village, on the contrary.' 'Melon towers? But these are watchtowers!' your mother said. 'Watchtowers?' I replied. 'Works of art!'

"I took the bicycle by the handlebars and we crossed the ditch at the side of the road... We'd hardly taken ten steps along a footpath when we heard yells. 'I can see you, I can seeee youuu! Thieves - st-eal-ing! Thieves stealing th' me-l-ons!' They were shouting at us, from the melon towers. We turned back, and the yells started again, but the voices were different. 'Hey! Good people! Come and honour us!' When they took us for thieves, about four of them were shouting at us, but now they were all calling, from every side. We tried to find the road to the village - yes! You've got it, some of them ran behind us and others came out in front of us, on the main road, to cut us off... We couldn't go off like that, without having a bite to eat; we had to try some and see, to honour the fruits of their labour - the melons, that is. We ate a slice, two, three; at first it was good for us, because we were hot and thirsty - but it wasn't proper to taste one man's and not to honour the melons of the next, and the rest of them - especially when they heard that we had come to be teachers in their village... Our Basarabians, they say of themselves: welcoming people, they enjoy having guests. But sometimes you feel like knocking them out with the bowl, or the tray, or the pitcher they're pushing at you. 'But 'ave some more! 'Onour us again! But 'ave a taste o' this as well...just a tiny bit...' - and that's what they're like when they bring in the harvest, when they kill a pig and when there's a wedding, baptism, funeral, or when they've made a special meal and they see that somebody's walking past along the lane... Luckily, your mother knows how to refuse a Basarabian without offending him - this time she said that...she was pregnant and had to be careful...

"And so we escaped the watermelons, but not the melon towers... Really the watermelons were just a pretext: 'Melons 're made by God, but what d'y think of...?' - that is, the things they had made with their own hands... Speaking sincerely, I'd never seen the like. In the army I had been through Bukovina and Oltenia, I knew what a wooden house was, the door painted with flowers, the carved pillars. I'd seen in photographs the wonders to be found in Maramures - and later, even round here in Ciocalteni, a marsh town, many of the houses had wooden verandahs, to say nothing of the cemetery, where the crosses were beautifully carved and made of oak... But the 'work' of the Manians... Some of them on three pillars, others on four, but even some on six or eight! - and only made of good strong oak from the forest (Mana was a clearing in the heart of the Orhei Forest). Few of the pillars were made from one piece of wood alone, finishing where the tree trunk ended - six or seven metres high - most of them were pieced together. And they were all like that: the support pillars, the reinforced beams, the ladders with hand rails... I couldn't say enough about the 'lookout towers' - that's what they called the platforms - with balustrades and roof rafters - not a space the width of your palm that hadn't been adorned with flowers made with chisel, gimlet, axe or lathe. Some were completely covered with flowers (your mother would say *de-flowered*), others were in the process, but even those which looked finished would receive yet another little beam or yet another little pillar here or there, and goodness knows what other additions... Hutanu made himself a second melon tower, about twenty paces from the first - the old one, he said, was 'a tiny little thing' (it was about twelve metres high), and he 'really needed' another, 'taller one - so's I can see how the river flows towards Orhei!...' "

"But what about the roofs?" Mother said.

"The roofs! The poorest of them were made out of wooden tiles - but what wooden tiles! From oak that had been scalded then blessed by charms, then worked piece-by-piece, polished and sometimes coloured... On some of them, a section of the roof had the wooden tiles laid like 'carp scales', that is, rounded at the edges, another section like 'fir trees' and another like 'ears of corn...' "

"But what about the sheet metal ones?" said Mother. "Or Hutanu's 'tiny little thing' with the slate roof? - do you know what the miserable man did - and him with nine children who all went about without any clothes? He sold his cow, the idiot! And what do you think he bought with the money from the cow? Pieces of slate! Oh but no, not for the children to have something to write on, No! So that he had a 'black stone' slate roof!"

"But what did he do with the frames?" I asked.

Father laughed and Mother laughed. I still didn't find out.

Father:

"What about Morcov? He sold two hectares of land so he could buy metal sheet - not galvanised steel though (others had that - but only on the melon towers), he had to have copper plates!"

"If we hadn't been occupied by the Russians, in '40," said Mother, "he would have sold off all the rest: he was thinking about gilding the copper, poor man - because he'd seen it done in town, on the churches, gilded copper, golden Morcov!"*

"But the bell-towers..." said Father. "At one point it went so far that, over a radius of about a hundred kilometres, people couldn't find any little bells for the cattle, or for the Christmas Star. The Manians had bought up everything that

* *Morcov* - name also means *carrot* in Romanian.

38

jingled, so they'd have 'music' from the eaves - they stuck them on, or tied them to the ends of goose feathers, and when the wind blew..."

"What about Old Iacob's whistling pipes?" said Mother.

"I remember those," I said. "Or I remember the ones he made specially for us, for the house..."

"I remember those as well," said Mother. "I had to pay a man a whole day's wages to repair the school roof..."

"They made a nice whistling sound," I tried.

"They would have sounded even nicer whistling from his house!"

"But there wasn't enough wind there, the school was much higher, only good for... So that's it: you didn't like the 'works' of the Manians..."

"Of course we did. We li-ke-d them," Father said.

"I didn't," said Mother. "Only what Mitrofan did: you could tell *he* came from our way, a man of the forest. He knew his wood, the wood knew him... You could tell that the others came from the Russian Steppes, for them an oak tree was so rare that they thought it could survive anything, and for any length of time - that's why they didn't leave a corner without flowers on it. And, on top of that, they even dirtied the holy wood with paint - and to beat it all: blue paint! Burn the lot of them! The carvers and the carved! And as far as the roofs were concerned..."

"They were attractive," Father tried.

"They were barbarian," Mother said.

"Just children, the Manians," I said.

"Yes, that's right", said Mother. "The melon towers: toys - but expensive ones... All the time, all they had was spent on...those poles with holes in them - and painted ones! - instead of crawling out of their underground caves and walking on two legs, like people..."

"I don't understand," I said.

"Neither did we, at the beginning," said Father. "When we first saw the melon towers, we thought that the Inspector had been lying to us, and that it wasn't a 'difficult' village; we thought that the houses, even if they weren't decorated with so-so-so many flowers, they'd at least have...houses... And when we reached the village..."

"The Inspector hadn't lied to us at all!" Mother said sharply.

"Not really, no," Father laughed. "The bumptious, as your mother called them, had made themselves watchtowers with little flowers, copper, slate, and even wanted to have gold. But their *houses*... hovels not houses! Together with the animals! They'd make a fire on the ground, in the middle of the one and only room, and the smoke would come out..."

"The smoke didn't come out all that much!" said Mother. "If something came out, it was usually flames - and off went the pit-house!"

"What, did all the Manians live like that?"

"Not every one of them, there were a few houses - Old Iacob's, Severin's..."

"That's why the school was so late in being built," said Mother. "Your father had to teach them how to build houses first. He had to pull them out of their burrows by the ears, like rabbits - the Inspector hadn't lied to us..."

"Perhaps they made themselves such tall and beautiful watchtowers to compensate for the low standard..." I tried but stopped, as Mother was looking daggers at me. But she was laughing:

"Perhaps, why not? And as we pulled them up to ground-level they shortened their...works of art, and reverted to the norm..."

"But you still haven't told me - what did they do up there, in the watchtowers?"

"Your father told you: up there, they put more flowers on, painted the roof inside; and when there was absolutely nothing more they could do, they built another one - even taller and..."

"But you were saying that they made them, so they could

move their backsides from the porch - didn't they sit in them, like on a *calidor*, but higher up? Didn't they watch the world go by from the heights?"

"Of course they did, but only the people that interested them: passers-by whom they'd shout at, at first, as if they were thieves; then, they'd force them to 'honour' their watermelons - in fact, they only wanted to show the strangers how high, how bedecked with flowers and how expensive their watchtowers were..."

No-Rabia
(or, *Ba* vs. *Be*)

"You tell me, then..."

The teacher in Father. I still don't know what he was asking me to tell him, but then I *did* know: it wasn't an examination, it was a lecture. All teachers begin a new lesson with a recapitulation of the previous one. However, this time I was wrong, because Father:

"...Why is it that foreigners, non-Romanians, say and write *Bessarabia* and not *Basarabia* like us Romanians, us Basarabians?"

"For the same reason that we, non-Bulgarians, say and write *Bulgaria* and not *Balgaria* like them, the Bulgarians; and that we, non-French, write and say *Burgundy* and not *Bourgogne*..."

"No, it's not like that," Father said. "It's not for the same reason. When we say and write Bulgaria and Burgundy, we do so because those were the Latin names and because that's how they came into the Romanian language. Whereas, in the case of Basarabia... Listen to me: when the Russian took the form *Bessarabia* from the great German and French cartographers, he gave it a particular meaning, because he was planning to conquer it."

"Seriously? Was it really like that?"

"Exactly what I'm telling you. As opposed to the other conquerors and occupying forces, the Russian has a great big heart, as big as a cartwheel. A Russian isn't Russian unless, before he sticks the knife in your back, he kisses you on the cheek, explains to you why he, poor soul, has been forced, cursed and condemned to do it to...and there you go, in the twinkling of an eye. But you can be sure *he* will be the one to suffer the torments of hell. God chose him for this kind of work: to help you, to liberate you, to teach you, to give you the shirt off his back today, because that shirt was yours anyway, yesterday..."

"Don't you think we're straying from...?" I ventured.

"No, not too much, only enough to remember that the Austrian, the Turk and the German never wasted any time explaining, justifying himself to those who'd been occupied, or at most said: 'I am stronger, I am right!' - full stop. However, the Russian wouldn't be Russian any more if, before eating you up completely, he didn't kiss you on the cheek, stick his tongue in your mouth, beg your forgiveness, *him* - from *you*, for what he's about to do to you, and say 'Forgive me, little father, dear heart, I'm a vile man, a worm - I'm guiltyyyy!...' "

"Don't you think we're getting into Dostoevsky now? Don't you think we should get back to *Ba* vs. *Be*?"

"Oh yes, Ba..., Be..., we'll get back to that, but after we talk about how the Russian is a scoundrel who only wants you to think he's a do-gooder; an occupier who asks you, obliges you to call him: *liberator*; a devil who won't leave you in peace until you call him an angel - and if you don't want to, too bad for you... In 1812, when they stole half of Moldavia from us, wasn't it a happy event, huh? It was a hard, well-deserved reward, for which the Russian had had to work conscientiously for a long, long time before the...battle. He had to toil, as under a yoke, to arrive at the explanation he was going to give afterwards, he prepared speeches as if he were talking about a great battle..."

"What speeches? What explanation?" I helped him.

"What else could they have been? That the thing he had stolen wasn't there to be stolen, Heavens above! it was there...to be 'found', he had found it covered in dust in the back lane. Goodness, how could he steal? How could he snatch a chunk of Moldavia? That kind of thing wasn't done. And who from? From an ally, from someone he was protecting, from a host? Ah, no!, those were enemy rumours! And if he did take anything, he didn't snatch it from the Moldavian, he received it - as spoils of war - from the Turk! That's how it was! If you said to him, 'But look, Ivan: this land is ours, Romanian, the people on this land are Romanian, man!' (Moldavia wasn't completely free, mind you, but it was only a vassal state of the Turks, it wasn't occupied, like Greece, Bulgaria, Serbia and even Hungary, which belonged to the Pashas for a while.) '...Besides, this time you've come to me as a friend, as a protector; and this time you've settled yourself here as if you were at home, you've spread yourselves over the whole land, my Moldavia; and this time you'd set off with your army to defend Christianity - and (for only six years this time) you've been milking me dry, making me rummage around the granaries, the cattle pens and even under the blankets... And then, when the show's over and you get around to beating our enemy, the Turk, you charge *me* taxes? You take half of *my* country from *me*?"

"A sensible question - but what would Ivan say?"

"Ivan? Like any Ivan: 'Little father, dear brother, precious friend of my tortured soul, how can you say such hard words which, look, are making my heart bleed... You mean to say that I have worn myself out, in the name of Christ, to save you from the Pagan, to free you from the accursed Turkish yoke, and you, ingrate that you are...' - and Ivan cries, cries tears as big as plums... And you, Moldavian ox that you are, feel God-knows-how, because you've caused grief to the poor Christian... But a fact is a fact and theft is a crime, so you don't let yourself be taken in: 'You've worn yourself out, not for the love of me or out of a desire to convert the non-Russians under the Turks to Christianity, but for the love of Tarigrad, that's your dream! For more than a century, the pair of you have been stewing, pushing each other around, punching and kicking each other under the table - but only on our land, the land of the miserable wretches you boast you've freed from the Turkish yoke. Bugger off back to where you came from, to the land of your fathers, into the swamps under the silver birches and the unexplored Steppes! Or take yourselves in hand and go to your rival, and fight it out in the Anatolian Ravines, put each other's eyes out over there! Until the Last Judgement, when the Reaper comes and sends you home to learn tomorrow's lesson!' "

"If you were the Reaper, you'd make fine history!"

"I'd make it with a stick and give them all the cane - what, don't you think my history would be good?"

"But what else would you say to him?" - trying to get Dad to talk about *Be* and *Ba* at the same time.

"I'd ask him what kind of man he was -' You're Christian, hm? And Orthodox as well?' 'Russian-Christian,' he'd reply. ...In 1878 when, in exchange for the help we'd given beyond the Danube - I say help, because they asked for it - it was the Christian-Russians who snatched our provinces in Basarabia, which we'd won back after the Crimean War. In any case, they told us that they gave us, in exchange, not only...independence, but also the Dobrogea! In exchange! I'd say, 'But listen, my man, exchange means you give something of your own, not something you've stolen from me! If you'd given, for example, Novgorod in exchange, but not Cahul, Ismail, I mean - *real* Basarabia!' "

"Have we got back to the point?"

"We have. I'd say, 'So where, Ivan, did you get this little notion of *Be*ssarabia from? I know - and I know better than you do, you who in those days were still crawling around on four legs in the peat, kissing the hem of the Khan's robe... I know,' I'd say, 'of a *Ba*sarabia - between the place where the river Danube bends around Galati and the mouth of the river Prut, broadly speaking Cahul and Ismail - that's what the place was called at one time after Basarab the First, prince of Wallachia, who took it from us, from Moldavia...' "

"Yes, he did... He stopped there as well and, like any

good Christian, carved his name on a willow tree with his penknife..."

" '...But that's what happened, ages ago, in the fourteenth century. We Moldavians didn't talk of Basarabia, Moldavia was divided into the Upper Country, up there in the North, the line where the river Prut crossed didn't matter, and into the Lower Country, further south, where similarly the Prut didn't count, because it didn't even cut across the Lower Country. Anyway, the little bit which was called Basarabia (other people called it that for a short time as well), it was lucky if it was as big as 5,000 square kilometres, but you, Ivan Bolovan, you cut Moldavia up into North and South, using the bed of the river Prut as the border, and then called nearly 50,000 square kilometres *Be*ssarabia! How's that? Why?' "

"And what would Ivan have to say to that?"

"Ivan'd say: 'Little father, dear brother, precious heart! But it's not true at all that the name of the region comes from a Basarab of yours - in fact, I haven't even heard of him. Let me tell you where the name of the land comes from, the land we Russians won from the pagan Turk, shedding our own, Russian, blood over it: the fact is, it is called Bessarabia because we, with our swords, drove out the Arabs - that's what we also call the pagan Turks and Tartars. After every single Arab was gone, we called the region by the name which was most suitable, that is, *Bez-Arabia*, which in your language would be translated as *Without Arabs*...' Well, what do you think about that, then?"

"What can I say? Where did you get the idea from?"

"From a book," Father replied. "Why, don't you think it's true?"

"Even if it's not, it could be. I know another little anecdote..."

"But it's not an anecdote! It's historical fact!"

"All right, well then I know another historical fact about Moldavia. In 1812 our people were protesting and asking for explanations, to use your words: 'Well, our Russian brothers, you said that you would free us from the Turks and then you go and steal half our country...?' To which the Russians came up with the following story... It seems that they can never explain things directly, they have to resort to parables - it's more poetic and the time passes (in their favour, of course), while the victim can boast that, in the meantime, the thief paid him the honour of having a long conversation with him... And so, the Russian replied, 'Let's say that you are a sheep; and let's say that the Turk is, inevitably, a wolf... good... So what happens? This is what happens. The wolf, a wild beast, seizes the poor sheep and gobbles half of him up. The other half of the sheep bleats and asks for help - who from? From who else - from us Russians, always ready to shed our own blood for the freedom of others - because we get on quite well like that... But how can we get the sheep out? Half of it is in the festering mouth of the filthy wolf! There's no way other than getting a good grip on the free half, or in other words, *controlling* it.' "

"That's what they did! Exactly like that!" said Father. "What does it matter that historical facts tell us, at that time, the Turkish wolf didn't have any teeth left in his mouth; and if you'd only tapped him on the back of the neck, he would have put it down? What does it matter that the wolf hadn't seized the Moldavian sheep, but the Bear gobbled up half of him anyway - the half that was probably crying for help..."

"However, in '39, the German wolf had gobbled up a good part of the Polish sheep, when the Bear came rushing to his help - to the aid of the German, of course - with the sheep bleating in his ear...it could only be to their advantage..."

"That's how it is! The wolf - whether he's Turkish, Austrian, or like in '39, Hitler - has never claimed that he was rescuing or liberating. The right of the wolf, of the strongest one! However, our brother the Russian...the ridiculous thing is, that because the professional diplomats are always repeating this fallacy about 'help', even the Russian in the street believes it... In prison camp, damn it, beyond the Arctic Circle, I was talking to a professor of history - not a lout, or soldier, or diplomat, or party activist - but to a professor, a Ukrainian, what's more. True, only at a high school, but a professor of history all the same! We ended up talking about the Baltic countries. I said, 'Why did you occupy them in '40?' He replied, 'We didn't occupy them, we liberated them.' I said, 'Who did you liberate them from? They weren't even occupied!' Pay attention to what he said to me. 'They weren't *then*. But if we hadn't moved quickly and liberated them, Hitler would have occupied them!' Do you like the logic? It flattened me. I brought up Poland, and said, 'How could you have attacked Poland from the east, when it had been destroyed pretty well by the Germans from the west?' The professor of history went berserk, 'I won't allow you to say such things! We didn't attack it, we liberated it - unfortunately, not all of it, I mean - right up to the Elbe...' "

"Didn't he mean to say: to the Oder? or to the Vistula?"

"That's just what I asked him myself - what would he want with the Elbe? We had the discussion in '42, the Elbe was...not the Volga... I knew that in their early days, the Slavs had set off for the West. I remembered something about Charlemagne ordering the construction of a defensive wall, like the Roman walls at *their* borders. He called it *sorabicus* - from: Serbs, the brothers or cousins of our Serbs..."

"Yes, but that happened a long time ago, before they were converted to Christianity..."

"What's Christianity got to do with expansionism? Here's the proof: those who aren't Christians any more, the Soviets, not only dream of having Christian Byzantium, but also ...*right up to the Elbe*."

"It's the first time I've heard..."

"Well, now you have, get your finger out and do some reading! If you knew a bit about history...older history, you wouldn't be surprised any more, today, when you look at a map of Europe and see the Iron Curtain. There's nothing new about it at all: that robber Gruzin only fulfilled the Slavs' dream: if you look at a map, you'll see that the Communists occupy today what the Slavs occupied until Otto the Great, I mean approximately following a line from Kiev to Trieste - with one exception, which isn't really an exception: Austria, which is...neutral, but still under Russian influence. Do you think it was because of the apple blossoms that the Russians were banging the Devil's drum about the Elbe, a meeting on the Elbe, a border at the Elbe? No, my man! Not for the apple blossoms and not for any old reason, they still consider the Elbe to be the natural border between them, the Slavs, and...the non-Slavs. We've got to admit, they've shown respect for history. They did stop at the Elbe, although they could have pushed further on to the Rhine ...to the Atlantic - who would have stopped them? The Americans?"

"You've forgotten another exception: Yugoslavia..."

"If you really think Yugoslavia's been left out, because Tito didn't let the Russians occ...liberate them... There might not be any Russians in Yugoslavia - but isn't there Communism? And who's Tito, if he's not just a little Stalin at loggerheads with the big Stalin? But I haven't forgotten the real exception: Greece. Because, oh Lord! even Greece was occupied by the Slavs - true, only for just over two centuries, but it was enough to turn it into a cattle-field! Look, they were farmers, village people, every town or city, if it wasn't deliberately demolished, fell into ruin anyway; the indigenous population who hadn't fled into the mountains, or to Italy and Sicily were...'de-christianized', they became illiterate, they were...to put it into one word...*slavicized*. Yes, Greece was the only defeat Stalin suffered..."

"Are we getting back to the professor of history?"

"We are. Yes, about the 'help' given to Poland. After he said it was a shame that they hadn't reached the Elbe when they liberated it, he said, 'We liberated our lands in Belorussia and the Ukraine, the ones that arrogant Leah had stolen from us!' "

"And what about Basarabia?"

" 'But what happened with Basarabia?' I asked him. He said, 'What about *Bessarabia*? It's ours, it's Russian territory, and...hey, it has been since...' 'And...hey, it has been since when?' I interrupted him, '...from 1812 to 1918 and now, since '40, when you got your thieving clutches on it again!' 'What thieving clutches?' he said, 'It was ours anyway.'

" 'It was, after you stole it,' I said. 'You occupied Romanian land, with Romanian inhabitants, speaking the Romanian language...' 'The Moldavian language, not Romanian!' he said, 'and *Bessarabia* was, and still is Russian land, the majority who live there are Ukrainians! You Romanians stole it in '18, profiting from a temporary weakness in the young Soviet state, you attacked from behind, like common robbers, your army occupied part of the body of the Soviet Motherland...'

"I said, 'Look, *Comrade Professor*, listen to a little bit more history. You know better than I do, that after what you call the Great October Revolution, the Soviet government adopted a Declaration proclaiming the Rights of Nations - which allowed self-determination-to-the-point-of-separation - a law which your Ukraine profited from, proclaiming itself an independent republic on the 11th of January 1918, a law which my Romanians in Basarabia also profited from to proclaim on the 24th of January of the same year, 1918, the Republic of Moldavia - a decision which was taken not by armed forces, but by vote; and not only the votes of the Romanian majority, but also of the Ukrainian, Jewish, German, Bulgarian and Polish minorities. And on the 27th of March their parliament, the Council, requested union with Romania!'

" 'It's not true!' the professor jumped from his seat. 'The bourgeoisie and the capitalists, the activists for the monarchy and the upper classes who were all against progress profited from the weakness - a temporary one! - of the young Soviet state and they stole Ukrainian territory!'

"I said, 'Make up your mind, *Comrade Professor*, the land of Basarabia - let's say *Bessarabia* - is it Russian, or Ukrainian?'

"After he had looked into the distance for a while, blinking slowly and pursing his lips, he said, 'In any case, it doesn't belong to you, the *mamaliga*-eaters!' That's what they call us, white-bread eaters: *mamalijniki*... And my Ukrainian went on, 'We did the right thing, in '40, when we recovered it! It's Soviet territory!' "

"What logic!", I laughed. "Were you astonished, surprised?"

"Yes. At the time, I thought to myself: Well, fair enough... But this discussion took place in a prison camp: the professor had got 20 years for 'anti-Soviet activity'! The anti-Soviet was him, the professor of history, not me, a country teacher - and furthermore, he was Ukrainian! Really, for him to tell me that... But, listen, you tell me...(Father had become my teacher again) what was the *motivation* behind the Dictate of the 26th June, 1940, in which the Russians asked for the 'restitution' of Basarabia?"

"The motivation? For example: 'The secular unity of Bessarabia with the liberating Soviet Union?' or 'The majority of the population of Bessarabia should be Ukrainian'...?"

"No, not those - those are Molotovisms. Molotov, like any good smith, hammered them out well... Son-of-a-bitch, he wasn't a proletarian-worker, he was a nobleman, related to a great composer, Stravinsky, I think...or perhaps it was Scriabin... I asked you something else: not the reasons that appeared in writing, but the unwritten motives, transmitted orally by the Russian's best friend, the German... I'm talking about Hitler's boy in Bucharest, Frabricius..."

"Oh, right: 'The town of Odessa is situated too close to the Soviet-Romanian border, on the Dniester, and since a town cannot be moved for protection, the border will be moved a little bit further away - from the town...' "

"That was it! The b...! It wasn't a new idea, they'd used it with Finland in '39. 'The Soviet-Finnish border is far too close to the symbolic town carrying the name of Lenin; and since we cannot move Leningrad further back, give us Karelia so we can push the border forwards!' "

"Logical..."

"That's the logic of our little brothers in the East...I can't say I ever got to know 'the Russian people'; and in the camp I only rubbed shoulders with anti-communist Russians. Perhaps I didn't have the time, or the luck...but what happened was: I didn't come across one anti-communist or anti-Soviet Russian who wasn't a Russian through and through, a Russian chauvinist, a Great Russian or a Russian expansionist... He's suffered, pain emanating from every pore, he's still suffering today, like Christ - but once you start talking about Russia, extending the Empire, 'liberating' other countries - the land or the people - the very last Ivan, collective farmer or worker, semi-literate soldier or even worse: prisoner - a victim of the regime - would think...right up to the Elbe. He sees things the same way as the Tsars did, and in the same way as Stalin..."

"I think you're exaggerating," I said.

"Listen, I hope from the very bottom of my heart that I am exaggerating - but you tell me...what fact or proof are you basing yourself on, when you ask me not to exaggerate? God help me that I'm not making a mistake - for who am I to claim that I know what has been, and know what will be? A simple country teacher, who reads the books in his school library... But *facts*? Unfortunately, the *facts* about the Russian... Fair enough, since '45 they haven't 'liberated' any

52

other hapless countries, other poor peoples - but a fact is a fact. What the Russian occupies, stays occupied. And when square kilometres come into it, he's not shy about 'defending' what he's occu...sorry, 'liberated' with tanks - just look at Berlin, or Budapest, and there'll be others, heaven knows..."

Heaven (or not heaven) knows. Father died in 1967. He didn't live to see 'the others': Prague, Kabul...

Poor Dad, he really hoped with all his heart that he was exaggerating when he said what he did about the Russians.

Long Live Gutenberg!

I'm sitting on the *calidor* of the house in Mana. And I'm shaking. I'm shaking because I was shaking then and, although I can't remember it, I have assimilated it and it has become part of me.

I'm sitting there and I'm shaking - but when you think about it, why shouldn't such memories, things, events still have their impact today - events I did actually witness though I was less than five years old at the time? Now I'm told that I wouldn't have been able to register them, to preserve them. Agreed: some "memories" were created for me and were reinforced by the stories I heard of other people's memories, their own, the memories of adults, at the time. However, there are others, passive scenes, key scenes, moments, states of mind which, although they "reached" me later (even today), trigger true recall, a succession, a step-by-step (or stone-by-stone) descent until they go so far back, not only to the age at which, it's said, you actually have the power to form "direct" memories, but even further back, to birth itself. But if I don't get a grip on myself and make a special effort to control my thoughts, which are advancing by retreating back there, I'll end up over on the other side of beyond.

I'm sitting on the *calidor* of the house in Mana and shaking. Father has been "pulled in". They pulled him in, I didn't see just how, but that's what people were saying. Mother had gone down into the village, to order a sleigh. It's said that they, the ones who pulled Father in, were pulling him into Orhei, and that there, she would have the right. To speak to Dad. There, she's allowed to; at home, here, she's

54

not. If I'd been in her place, I wouldn't have believed them. Mother did believe them and had gone to order a cart to have the right at Orhei, and had left me in Old Iacob's care. But what did I want with Old Iacob's care? I left and came back here, home, to our place. I could have stayed down there in the yard: if I'd poked around the pile of ashes with a stick, I would have found some embers and spines and covers which hadn't completely burned to ashes, and I could have warmed my hands. And my heart. But look, here I am, sitting on the *calidor* and not warmed up.

I was sitting right here yesterday as well, in the afternoon, when they came - in a *car*! I didn't know that they were in the car, the car drove past alone, down there, to the middle of the village; afterwards it came back and stopped right outside Old Iacob's. The car was at Old Iacob's, but they were here. Three of them with three leather trench coats, three pistols, really long ones, in three long wooden casings. One pistol, when he came into the courtyard, said to me, on the *calidor*:

"*Gde assassor?!*"

I had learned four or five words of theirs, and I knew that they were asking me where he was. I went down two steps and said, I said that here in this village that kind of thing doesn't happen, because it's not right - perhaps in other villages. And then the other one said in my language - he said:

"You are the son of the *assassor*? Where is your papka?"

Then I understood they meant Father; and I also understood that Father had assassinated someone, that was why the car was there: to pull him in. I got down from the *calidor* and ran as fast as I could across the yard, jumped over the stile to Old Iacob's - where had Mother gone? (It wasn't for me to know, but she was with Aunt Domnica, hiding in the large old stove.) It took the grown-ups a long time to explain to me later that they had pulled Father in, not for assassinating someone, but because of his books and

55

flag, and that they had said teacher - *assessor* in Russian - and that obviously teachers in their country, in Russia, were occupied with assassinations, and not what Mother and Father were occupied with.

Much later, Father told me:
"I was in a lesson, in the afternoon, with the second to fourth years, when the door opened. Without even knocking, in came... a comrade: trench coat, oilskin *sleapka* hat, boots, Nagan pistol at his hip. In the past...in the past he wouldn't have even taken a second step: I would have thrown him out of the classroom by the scruff of his neck, with my foot up his backside, like I did to one little prick of an Inspector, before the Surrender - even though *he* had been wearing a nice new hat, not a proletarian *sleapka*... Only I'd learned a few things in six months under the Soviet regime... I clenched my teeth and despite everything, said to the class, 'Stand up straight, children, salute the Comrade, show him, yourselves, that he's come into a house of education.' The children stood up and saluted him, all together... But the Comrade stood, how can I say it? as hard as steel... *And* he was bow-legged. The oilskin *sleapka* was still on his head. I forgot the 'diplomacy' I had learned, grabbed the thing off the idiot's head, opened the door and hurled it into the corridor..."
Father sighed, laughed and shook his head.
"Well, now I'd dived into the water, I might as well swim: so I went to seize the Comrade by the collar, to send him after his hat. But he walked past me and went outside by himself. And he was laughing! I went out after him, he was picking his hat up from the ground - he wasn't laughing any more. He said, 'You haven't changed a bit, Teacher-Sir,' in Romanian. I looked at him. I seemed to know him from somewhere..."
"Do you remember when you caned me so hard you made my hand bleed?" he said.

" 'I've had to cane lots of children... But I don't remember ever having made someone's hand bleed,' I said.

" 'We'll make you remember, we've got the most advanced methods for bringing memories back - but what about calling me: stinking Jew? Do you remember that?' "

Father was trying hard to keep smiling. With rather unsteady hands, he lit another cigarette from his last one, which he hadn't even finished smoking.

"I said, 'Now I know who you are, you're Sapsa, Avrum the shopkeeper's son; you were a pupil of mine in '34, about two years ago you fled across the River Dniester...so you're back. From what you're wearing I can see how powerful you've become - have you come to pull me in because six or seven years ago I gave you the cane? So hard your hand bled?' He said, 'And because you wanted to hang me - look, the scar's still on my neck; and because you raped my sister Roza, that's why she drowned herself in the lake; and because you wrung my father's beard, after you'd smashed the house windows; because...we'll find a reason, don't worry...'

"I looked at him - my legs had frozen: I knew that anything *I* said would have been in vain; that anything *he* said would have been listened to. I'd rot in Siberia!

"And so I said: 'Then let me get some things...' 'No', he said, 'for the time being we're not taking you to our place in Orhei: for now you can hand over everything you didn't hand over last autumn, when Soviet power was established - get the flag out!'* he said, and then he said, 'We know you keep it hidden in the house, in the leather suitcase - in the big one, not in the little one....' "

"Was it true?" I asked, "Is that where the flag was? That means that someone who knew our house..."

"That went through my mind as well for a second: someone who knew not only the house but the suitcases as

* Banner held by the chief of a paramilitary territorial unit - who, in a village, was usually headmaster of the local school.

well... But I relaxed - in a manner of speaking - because the flag wasn't, one, in the house, and two, in the large suitcase, I'd hidden it elsewhere, the proof being - we've still got it today. Your mother had sewn it inside a blanket, straight onto the wool... One of their methods; they frighten you with God knows what, and you blurt everything out, like a fool...

" 'Wait until you look in the small one,' I said, and then I said, 'Where did you get the idea that I called you *stinking Jew*?' I might not have been in the habit of kissing Jews, but I didn't say that kind of thing either. Why? I don't know...but I know I didn't say that.'

"Sapsa started to laugh - he simpered, 'And so what if you didn't say it? You didn't say it, but your kind have said it, bourgies, anti-Semites! If you said it or didn't say it - what does it matter, that's not going to prevent the progress of history: it only matters that you're a teacher of the bourgeois, Romanian, reactionary kind! It only matters that all Romanians are reactionaries, that all bourgies are anti-Semitic!' I said, 'Look, now I'm sorry that I didn't cane your hands until they bled, to knock some sense into you and teach you to think.' Then Sapsa took two steps back, and got the Nagan out: 'For what you've just said, I can put you into prison right now, the Comrades would congratulate me, they'd reward me for crushing a viper, but I want you to see that we Bolsheviks aren't like you bourgie Romanians, like you anti-Semitic boyars...' I looked at the gun he had... My knees were shaking, firstly because I felt he was telling me the truth, he could have put me into prison right then, whom would he have to answer to? His kind? The ones who had taught him to behave and think like that? Secondly, because...I hadn't 'sovietized' myself: I didn't understand, couldn't accept - in myself, of course - that someone could say such things without even blinking...not only lies but nonsense - and lots of it, nearly all he said. Where would you start, to try and make some sense out of it? I said to him, in

58

a quieter, more...friendly voice: 'Listen, Sapsa, you know me, your family have known me for more than ten years, how can you say so many stupid things to me in one breath? You know me, but I know you as well, aren't you the boy...the man who...' 'You don't know me,' he snapped under his breath, cutting me short. 'You don't know me, I don't know you!' - his cheeks were dripping with sweat. And then he said, 'Send the children home!' I sent them home. 'Now get out and hand over to the Soviet power all the books to be purged!' "

"So, that's how *Gutenberg* began...," I said.

"That's how it ended," Father said, without smiling.

"I said, 'But I handed them over when power was established...' 'We have information that you've hidden them in the house,' said Sapsa. 'I haven't hidden anything,' I said, 'I took my own personal books back out of the school library, the ones I'd bought with my own money, out of my salary...' Sapsa: 'Money extracted from the labouring masses, from the sweat of the proletariat, of the working classes! Get all the bourgeois books out and hand them over to Soviet authority!' 'How are they so bourgeois?' I said, 'You read them as well and didn't become bourgeois, your mother read them, your sisters...particularly Roza, who came around to see us only two days ago - what's bourgeois about the works of Creanga and Sadoveanu* or Tolstoy and Pushkin and...as a matter of fact, only recently I received books from...' 'Don't play Clever Dick with me!' Sapsa hurried me, 'What you've received now, under the Soviets, in Russian and in Moldavian are real books, good ones! I'm talking about your books, fascist, reactionary and bourgeois books, the opium of the people, because they're written in the Latin characters you Romanians use! Everything that's printed in Romanian letters is reactionary! Inimical! Capitalist! The Comrades

---

*Ion Creanga (d. 1889) and Mihail Sadoveanu (1880-1961), important Romanian writers of works on pastoral themes.

were right to ban them, so get 'em out and hand 'em over!' I asked, 'Do I have to give you the translations from Gorky, printed in the Romanian (Latin) alphabet?' 'Hand 'em all over ! We'll take them to our place in Orhei, and we'll decide what's good and what's bad for the people!' "

Father lit another cigarette, his hands were unsteady: another memory was causing him pain.

"What could I do? There was no way out. I had sent the children home, there were only the three of them and me in the school... Sapsa and another one of *them* went into the house...luckily you and your mother were at Old Iacob's; he was rummaging around, turning everything upside down. The third one, a kind of Tartar, took me back into the school to clear the library of everything that was 'inimical' - but there was nothing, I'd taken all the books in...the Romanian alphabet into the house. I couldn't talk to the 'Kalmuk', he didn't speak Romanian, and later on at Orhei, during the 'discussions' with Sapsa, I got the impression that he didn't even know much Russian... But as Sapsa would have said, 'What does it matter?' Ignorant as he was, he was perfect in the role of a NKVD secret policeman. He knew one word, only one, but what a word - *Davai!* and he was an expert when it came to shoving his antiquated old gun into my ribs, my stomach or into the back of my neck... At one stage, when Sapsa had made a pile of books in the middle of the house and asked me for some bags, I said to him, 'Why tire yourselves out carting them up to Orhei, leave them here, I'll burn them right here.' 'You burned them last autumn but here they are, intact - we're taking them with us, to headquarters, we've got a spanking new incinerator, it swallows up a truckload of Romanian books an hour.' I said, 'I'll burn them now, in front of you.' He consulted the others, the boss seemed to be the Tartar - and then he said, 'Burn 'em! But here and right now!' And so I burned them..."

"But what about when they beat you up? Before you

burned them or started shouting: '*Long live Gutenberg!*'?"

"Earlier on, in the school, I'd had a...discussion with Ghirei-khan, or whatever he was called: Ghireikhanov, Khanghirev... Anyway, we had a heated 'discussion', he was still pushing me around with his Nagan, saying '*Davai!*' all the time, and I lost my temper and told him he was a c... and to fuck off. In Romanian. But even though Khanov the Tartar didn't know a word of Romanian, and hadn't much of a clue about Russian, he knew the Russian swear-words alright - that's how you learn Russian: by swearing... And since that shameful word in our language comes from the Slavic... You know which one... The Tartar understood it! And he hit me about the head with his pistol. I tried to defend myself, I think I must have just caught him, and he started bellowing, the other two came from the house and... That's what happened..."

"Did Sapsa hit you as well?"

"I don't really remember, but no, I don't think he did too much. Or...yes he did, but only for appearance's sake...But after the Gutenberg thing he did. In fact, he hit me more than anyone. Later on, at Orhei, I gleaned a little, and in the camp I had plenty of time to deduce the rest: Sapsa didn't want it known, at Orhei, that he'd been the protégé of a certain Goldenberg from Tiraspol, one of their *kommissars* who'd let his mouth go and had been imprisoned for a while, or sent to Siberia - but how on earth was I supposed to know about their goings-on? And how on earth was Sapsa supposed to know that Gutenberg was someone completely different from that *kommissar* of theirs - he must have thought, confound it! that I was shouting, 'Long live...' - a name similar to Goldenberg's..."

"But why did you say that *you* burned the books? Let's say that I don't remember because I was only about five years old - but both Mother and Old Iacob, and other adults, said that *they*, your visitors, doused them with petrol, *they* set fire to them, *they* raked the ashes over with a fork..."

"What does it matter who doused them with petrol, who struck the match, who...kept the fire burning? Fair enough, they did...the NKVD agents. But wasn't that their mission, their profession? - to ruin, to destroy, to burn, to... Look, I don't know whether anybody's told you about this, but the second thing they did after they occupied us - I mean after the first wave of arrests - was to cut the forests down. They razed the Orhei forests. However, as the Russian always does, hack-handed, regardless: old trees, saplings, bushes, the lot. It broke our hearts. A forest isn't a strip of wheat or corn, and not only because it doesn't grow back within the year - we said to each other: the Russian's taking it all with him, over the river Dniester, all he can manage, he must think that he can't make much money from it here... But then the autumn rains came and you couldn't get into the forest - what would a Romanian have done? He would have waited for the ground to harden and freeze and then he would have gone in. But once a Russian, always a Russian: what he can't take, he breaks. He set fire to the wood - to the piles and stacks of wood already cut down and to the trunks still in the ground. Our trees were burning for weeks; in the summer, the village people had been forced out in tears to cut our forest down. Now they were crying again, burning everything that had been felled to the ground and everything growing out of the ground... At that time, when the forest was chopped down and burned, I was starting to learn a few things about the communist mind, not only in relation to the economy, but also to his sympathy for the forest..."

"Nevertheless, in '40 -'41 they had just started - they say that here and there you can find the odd oak tree now, or a sycamore or elm. At least the name is still there: the Forest of Orhei..."

"What they did to the people and the forest, they did to the books as well, the criminals - but I said to myself then what I say now: that is their profession, their mission - to destroy, to burn. While my profession is...the opposite. Your generation, those born after the First World War, make fun of us, when you talk about teachers you put inverted commas around the word 'apostle'... Not only did we call ourselves apostles but we believed with all our hearts that that is what we really were... We were the first, the pioneers, we weren't only teachers-of-books but we were teachers-of-everything; we weren't only looking after children, teaching them their ABC's and how to count, but also after their parents and people who didn't even have children at school. Do you realise? We taught them what they thought they'd known from their ancient ancestors onwards: agriculture. Mind, Mana was a special village, a 'difficult' case, made up of servants, not of peasants, made up of *souls*, not of freeholding peasants - but even in the true, Romanian villages the people who taught the villagers agronomy, veterinary medicine, hygiene were us, the teachers. The specialists appeared much later and even then they weren't taken seriously - they didn't know their... specialisation, those specialists who were sent here. They didn't need to, they'd come to Basarabia to make money, not for an apostleship... They say that Moldavian cuisine is varied and refined - the women teachers taught the refined Basarabian women to cook other things, in different ways... We didn't only bring knowledge about agronomy and hygiene to the villages, knowledge which had been entrusted to us by our teachers, but by our very presence there we accomplished much more than our actions alone did... I'm thinking about that idiot Sapsa, the opinions he formed beyond the river Dniester - that all teachers are anti-Semitic - I'll tell you something you won't read in any book or hear from the lips of any Romanian no matter how decent he is. The story's been told to the point of nausea by the Communists: the story of racism and anti-Semitism. We, the people who were at teacher training college together, all came from villages; in our villages, we had our Greeks, our Russians, our

Lipovans, our Gypsies, our Jews - they were different from us, but they were at one with us! The village is like a living body, it has to find its own...if not, harmony, then a kind of...how can I put it?...equilibrium, otherwise the village goes to pot. When we arrived at college, teacher training school, we learned, among other things, from the professors - and what good professors we had! - we learned how to get on with each other, if it wasn't possible to live singing the same tune or the same song (as the ballad goes), put it behind you and love will get you along - so, let's all live together in understanding: I, the Moldavian, will take care of the wheat and the cheese; you, the Lipovan, take care of the sausages and the ham; you, the Jew, keep the village shop; you, the Greek...and so on, or as they'd call it now: 'division of labour'. Or as you could also put it, no conflict of interest... Where do you find conflicts of interest? In the town, that's where the Greek, the Armenian and the Jew are all in competition against one another...have you got the message? In the village, it was 'our little Jew', in the town: The Jew - full stop... When the Theology College was founded at Chisinau, we also received the light, if I can say it like that, and our Basarabians discovered that our little Jew, or The Jew in the town wasn't a wretch with twelve children piled on top of each other in a stinking hovel, but was of historical significance! Zion and Kahal! An international asset! Once again then, we came from the village, we did our teacher training and to the village we returned. Cuzaism, the Iron Guard,* they didn't affect us - how could they? The Cuzaist policy followed one, indivisible line: '*Down with the Jews!*' - but how much further down could our little Jew get than the village shopkeeper? The Iron Guard's motto: '*Everything for an Acre of Land*'. But we had plenty of land; we didn't use the acre as a measure, an acre's nothing: we used hectares!

---

* *Cuzaism* - interwar fascist ideology and politics, led by A.C.Cuza. *The Iron Guard*, a political-military grouping whose formal name was The Legion of the Archangel Michael.

And besides: we Basarabians were supposed to have been backward, illiterate, when we united with Greater Romania; but I understood that the programme put forward by *our* Council, which had been voted upon, was so advanced that it was at least a hundred years ahead of the rest of the Romanians!"

"Hey, it wasn't quite so..."

"It was! Both socially and nationally - why do you think Marghiloman (conservative Romanian politician, died 1925) went on like that? To dilute it, bring it down, down to the level of the Mother Country. But even so, diluted, levelled-down, we hadn't forgotten it... Just let Avrum's Sapsa come to me and tell me that... Fair enough, it's not concrete proof of...philo-semitism, but the fact remains: we teachers brought, introduced non-Romanian dances to the villagers which hadn't been used at round-dances and weddings for decades..."

"The waltz, the tango?"

"Not only those, but the *shair* as well, a Jewish dance the Basarabians danced, without knowing and not really caring whose it was, or where it came from... The same went for the quadrille... But what I wanted to say: when your parents are semi-illiterate, and you do six years of teacher training (that's how much they used to do then) to return to where you came from and teach them, you, a little chip-off-the-old-block, how to build a house with their own hands, how to dig a well, how to rotate crops, how to cure animal and plant diseases, and when you teach them how to detach themselves from the animals, I mean - to make stables, cattle sheds, pigsties, henhouses... And especially when you persuade the peasants, who are unhealthily modest (shame can kill a man, especially in the country), you teach them, yes, to make latrines - more to the point, you even succeed!... However modest you might be, you feel kind of different. Sure, this 'different' has made some people run away with themselves, believe they're God, but I'm not

65

talking about them, I'm talking about the others, the real teachers... As you come to realise that your knowledge, acquired at school, Look! is being used for something, and you can touch it, then you become even more self-confident, and so... And so, don't put inverted commas around apostleship..."

"Mm, yes," I said. "Yes, let's get back to the books."

"All right, then. Who in the village was the symbol of literacy? The Teacher!"

"And the priest."

"Not in Basarabia."

"How's that? Everywhere the Church has been the last refuge, the last sanctuary..."

"Not in Basarabia."

"I know what you think about our Orthodox Church and you know what I think - but let's go back in time a little bit: in Bulgaria, in Greece, in Serbia, in spite of the terrible occupations - sometimes religious - Turkish - the Orthodox Church was a shield, sanctuary, and asylum. But you're saying not in Basarabia? Which was occupied, however...by Christians? Orthodox?"

"But listen to me, not in Basarabia, no. The Greek, when he took refuge in his church - he could at least escape there to forget about the Turk - which language did he hear? Greek. The Serb, the Bulgarian - which language did they hear? Not Turkish or Arabic, but Slavonic, a language belonging to their heritage, not the occupying force's. Whereas, the Basarabian, poor soul, in which language, even if only the church language, was he to look for (as you say) asylum, sanctuary, oblivion, protection? In his language, Moldavian? A few churches had started holding services 'in the language of the people', before 1812, but if the Russians had forbidden the use of the vernacular in the schools, how could they permit it in the churches? And especially since that was the 'tradition'? Which goes to say: occupied by the Russians; forced to learn Russian - it doesn't matter how much he had to put up with from the administration and the army - even in the church, the Basarabian heard the language of the occupying force..."

"But the Russians didn't impose it on us, Slavonic had entered the chancery and the church in the 16th century. And the spirit didn't possess us, like today...from the East, but from the South, from the Bulgarians, via 'the Greeks' - Cyril and Methodius... "

"You don't understand, do you, that I'm talking about the Basarabians, not about all Romanians? I repeat: the Basarabians, occupied by the Russians, couldn't escape from 'their Russian', not even in the church - so..."

"So, that's the explanation behind the fact that they remained - or they reverted to oral communication, to...illiteracy. But it seems that they didn't dislike the church music, or the music of the Slavonic text ..."

"You didn't either - when you were a child ... and wandered about the forest* - so the Russians wouldn't repatriate you to their country, as you used to say ... Can you remember, in Buia, by the sheepfold, how we sang in three voices, ... and then in four, five and six voices ...?"

"I remember. I like it still... But why say we sang in Slavonic? We were only singing la-la-la, without words, only the vowels...and especially O... I like it, but I find it a bit too much like opera, à la *Boris Godunov*..."

"And what's wrong with that? Isn't the liturgy opera? Or a play? Whatever I have against the Russians, their music, the liturgy...Russian to the very last pore..."

"It's too pathetic."

"Well otherwise, how are you going to wake that God up from His sleep? The Catholics whisper in His ear, the Protestants play the organ to Him - but us? We have to shout, bellow, and even then You hardly hear us..."

---

* The author here invokes one of the most famous lines of Romanian poetry, by Mihai Eminescu, 1850-1889.

"Calm down, He's not listening to *us*. Let's get back to the books: why do you insist that you burned them?"

"Wasn't I the one who threw them out of the window into the schoolyard?"

"But you didn't set fire to them!"

"So what? It felt like I did! You just don't understand: 'The school library', three-quarters of it, was made up of books we had bought, your mother and myself, from our meagre little salary. Because there weren't many, each book had its own history, another one, besides the one in the text... We were peasants, a peasant doesn't buy any old thing he sees, he weighs it up, works out the price, so he knows what he's getting for his money. Sure, it was a miserable little school library in a miserable little village in Basarabia - but they were books! It was a library... And, there you go, illiterate scoundrels and robbers stomp in with their leather boots and their *sleapkas* on their heads, rogues! At least if they had stolen them decently, if that's possible, I mean - to take them from you and keep them for their own use - but no! It was like they'd taken your horse from the stable and then killed it in front of your eyes in the courtyard. It doesn't even follow their principles, of 'equality': where everybody should have something, not just a few people... No: nobody should have anything! That's their equality. Luckily th..."

"Luckily there was Gutenberg, the inventor of the printing press - that was why you shouted '*Long live Gutenberg!*'?"

"Yes, that was why, but I was mistaken. I was young, naive, I said to myself that however many books the rogues burn, they can't burn the printing press, the invention... I was a fool. I realised, not in Basarabia after the surrender in '40 but in Romania, after the '44 surrender: there was no need for them, the security forces, arsonists by profession, to burn the books; they only had to put the fear of God into people who had books - nobody burns books so well as a book lover..."

"You're exaggerating: not even the arsonists burned all of them, nor did those who had books burn all they had. Some survived - I told you about how I 'appropriated' a few bagfuls of books in Transylvania at Seica Mare, I stole some from Astra as well and from Sibiu; but I wasn't lucky..."

"A few bagfuls! But what about the rest, though? And so, we're a race of people without papers and with only a few books - and look what happens, the 'enlighteners' from the East discover us! To burn them, the few we have."

"How would you feel about...what would you do with, for example, *The Complete Works of Stalin*. Wouldn't you burn it?"

"I'd like to toast your health for every 'series' of *Complete Works* - and not only of Stalin's - I've set fire to, in the offices that used to be our house..."

"So, you *have* burned a book?"

"A book, that? That wasn't a book, it was..."

"So, for you, Sapsa's book wasn't a book; just as for Sapsa, your books in...the Romanian alphabet, weren't good, true books - in that case, let's all shout together: '*Long live Gutenberg!*' "

The Romanians Are Coming!

I'm sitting on the *calidor* of our house in Mana. It's Sunday morning.

So far so good: it's the morning and it's a Sunday - or perhaps it's only a holiday? - whatever the case, from this point on begin only my own memories.

I haven't got a calendar for 1941, to find out what date the first Sunday fell on after the twenty-second of June. And even if I had one, what use would it be? Most likely it would confuse me - I have my own internal calendar which tells me that perhaps, perhaps, that day was neither a Sunday nor an important holiday in other people's calendars - for example St Peter and St Paul's Day... It's useless, now, to try and find "signs" which might have made me think that, back then, or from which I would have known that it's Sunday - not another - not any other day of the week.

I could talk, for example, about the peaceful festive spirit in the air, typical of holidays in summer and in the country; or I could give another example and describe the cheerful harmony of the church bells (calling the faithful to the service); or I could talk at length about the pleasure of being lazy on Sundays, in the mornings, in summer, in the countryside.

But no: it wasn't peaceful, not a holiday with church bells, nor lazy. Right. Church bells? Where from? The bells hadn't rung for a long time. Since the Occupation, our church was closed - for the time being - for a year long's "time being", and if it was to be opened again for a "time being", where was the priest? There wasn't a priest! (Ours, as it happens, was in refuge in Romania, not...in Siberia.) Like those from the neighbouring villages. As for the

70

monasteries (Hirova, for nuns, about three kilometres over the hill; Curchi, for monks, to the left, to the west again about three kilometres away, and Tabora, for nuns, a bit further than Curchi), they had been dissolved and turned into clubs, state farms and storehouses, while the monks and nuns..., God help them wherever they were in Siberia.

I must emphasise the point: from that holiday morning, all my memories are mine alone - from the age of five years and about nine months. Real memories, that is, drawn from me (into my memory), chains of events, not only static images (for example, like the burning of the books in the yard, and Father dancing naked from the waist upward, with a bottle of brandy in one hand, hopping about around the "pyre" on the snow and shouting - a terrified man but rejoicing all the same: "*Long live Gutenberg!*"). From that morning onward, I began to record my own memories, like adults, in succession: to consciously receive and deposit the things which were happening right around me...and gaps don't interrupt the chain of events, as they did before, now they just act as a filter.

I must emphasise: from that morning onward I started accumulating, collecting, setting aside and hoarding. That's why I've become so rich... And it's not impossible that the impression, the certainty of it being a Sunday is due to, and why not? an early commemoration like a christening. For that day to have been observed for two reasons, the saint's day of my brother, dead, and of me, as yet not dead - it must have been the twenty-ninth of June - and hopefully, the real, historical calendar won't contradict me.

Later on I was to find out (thus supplementing my "pre-memory") that, "for a good week or so, you could hear the guns over the Prut"; and that, at night, "you couldn't see the stars, the sky was so red" (to the west) - therefore: THE ROMANIANS ARE COMING - from the Prut.

And so: on this holiday morning, I was sitting on the *calidor*. Above and between the roofs of the houses, descending the gradual slope towards the main road, I could see; I could see, below the line of old willow trees at the edge of the common, I could see, *cars and soldiers*. For the first time, I was seeing them, *me*, with my own eyes. I saw them and was surprised. Where must they have come from? I'm surprised now, to complete the feeling of surprise I had at the time (you can't be sure about anything in this world - what if I wasn't surprised at all?)

I could also see: smoke billowing out from below the willows. Then I heard: roar of cannons - some the same, others different. I could see, higher than high in the sky, puffs of white smoke like dandelion clocks. While from the other side, I could hear the windows clanging. And I could feel: the floor of the *calidor* whirring, as if a cart were upside down with its wheels spinning round beneath me. I could hear another sound, which started to get nearer and nearer, enveiled us - then unveiled us and went away again. But I couldn't see the noise.

Mother, in her night-shirt, barefoot, her hair uncombed, came out to the doorway behind me and shouted:

"Don't sit there. Good heavens! Get in immediately!"

I didn't go in. What? Was I stupid? Especially since Mother was busy for a good length of time and was otherwise occupied... She was opening all the windows of the house as wide as possible, then she crossed the yard in her bare feet, and after a short while, opened the windows of the school as well, all of them.

I wonder whether I asked her why she was opening the windows? Perhaps I did - in which case she didn't answer; perhaps I didn't - I knew why: so that "the sound" didn't break the windows.

Just look at Old Iacob. He went out into their yard, to my left. He was dressed in the black trousers he wore on Sundays (See? What did I tell you?) and his black leather, high-heeled, shiny boots which were flared at the knees.He was wearing his hat but his chest was bare - he mustn't have

72

got around to putting his shirt on, or he'd taken it off in the doorway so he'd have something white to wave about up in the air. With one hand, he was keeping his wide-brimmed black hat on his head, and with the other he was making white circles above the black and shouting - shouting as if at the sheepfold, on the other hill:

"Here, he-e-re! Come on, ov-er he-ee-ere!"

From my place, I could see three courtyards across the road: Maxim's to the left; Simion Cristea's straight ahead, and, to the right, a quarter of it hidden by the school's cornel tree, Old Andrei's yard.

Simion Cristea was running to and fro in the yard, dodging a child here and there, stumbling over a tool he had forgotten about - all the while offering a bottle of wine up to the sky. He was bellowing, like in a tavern (we didn't have one at Mana, but I'd heard from the grown-ups):

"Come on, let's have a drink, boys! Get a move on, faster!"

Faster, get a move on - let's drink to their coming.

Old Andrei came into sight in his courtyard. In his drawers. His hand was held like a ledge over his eyes and he was rolling his head from one side to the other, following the humming sound that was getting closer and then further away - in between the dandelion clocks of smoke. And I heard Old Andrei say:

"Well, lads, well... Y've come in th' end..."

Next to him was Old Andrei's old wife: with one hand on the old man's shoulder, the other waving what she had at hand toward the sky: her little white apron which tugged up the front of her skirt - I could see her old pins - thin, black and crooked. A step behind them was Duda, their grand-daughter. She was doing the same as her grandmother, only she didn't have an apron on and was waving and shaking the hem of her dress - from the *calidor*, from our house, I could see even further up than she'd told me one day that it was proper to see, that day when she told me to look up there

73

and not down below.

It was like a wedding in Maxim's yard: Maxim had climbed up on top of the cart from which the horses had been unharnessed in front of the house. He waved his hat around, then grasped it between his knees and looked up into the sky through his eye-glass (little pretzel rings he'd made with his fingers) and told them down below:

"That's one of our Romanians - shout fer him t' come!"

Maxim's wife and daughters-in-law were shouting, yelling and shrieking like nervous hand-maidens and waving their handkerchiefs around. The swarthy daughter-in-law, the devilish Ileana, was standing with one leg raised on the hub of a wheel; one hand clinging on to her father-in-law's shirt and the other pointing at something, I couldn't see what - down there, straight ahead, on the ground: "Gheorgheeee! Come on right down! I'm waitin' for you, the table's set!" - and she was still pointing to the ground, straight ahead: I knew what it was about: Gheorghe was her husband, caught "on the other side" after the Surrender - it didn't matter that he wasn't a pilot - if only he'd come anyway!

"Th' other one's one o' theirs!" Maxim announced. "Bugger off t' where you came from! Go 'n' hang yerselves!"

The women were hooting and yelling. Ileana - I could see her perfectly - was standing with her backside bare. It was whiter than white.

Mother came down the school stairs towards me:

"I thought I'd told you to get into the house!"

She did, but I'm not. Anyway, now Mother had stopped in the middle of the yard and was looking up into the sky. The hum was getting louder. She raised one of her hands up as well, but only to shoulder height. The next minute she realised she was only in her night-shirt and barefoot; so she ran into the house with her hands crossed chastely over her chest...

And just as well she did: the sky darkened there and then - but only for a second - the humming grew so loud it was like a fist bursting through the sky. A whirl of dust sprang up from the very place Mother had been standing just a short while ago; then splinters shot from the fence which separated us from Old Iacob's.

"Hey! Not here!" bellowed our old neighbour, letting go of his hat in order to threaten the sky with his fist. "Don't give it t' us, boy, give it t' those thieves, heyyy!" - and he pointed in the direction of the common...

Mother didn't see what had been happening behind her; she grabbed hold of me by the shoulder without sparing any pain and dragged me into the house, me nearly on all fours. I wasn't going to let her. I didn't want to be in the house. I wanted to be outside, I wanted to be on the *calidor*. To see and to hear. I struggled and tried to get away from her. She gave me the back of her hand - I didn't care about the smack and tried to get outside again.

I don't know whether it was actually because of the smack, and just after that the fight on the floor of the hall (with Mother on top of me) or because Mother, who had the feeling that something was going to happen (after hearing the whizzing of the bullets) had forced me to lie down and then had lain down on top of me - I only know that my nose was crushed onto the floorboards and it was hurting, and that I was crying.

When I got up, whining, I had to avoid pieces of glass from a broken vase. Through the door of the living room, which was open, I could see - I could see nothing: nothing but dust.

"You have t' leave, Missus," Old Iacob said, pressing his hat politely to his chest (he'd got dressed in the meantime - he'd fastened the buttons of his "redingote" which was also black, right up to his chin). "We're goin' t' have a right time 'ere, a devil of a time, sorry for th' swearin', that's men's business... So you'd better leave wi' th' littl' boy, I'll look after th' house..."

Mother brought things out of the house, suitcases,

bundles, packages, and took them over the stile. Old Iacob was always ahead of her - at the stile telling her that she shouldn't tire herself out, that this was men's work. Mother didn't take any notice of him, carried the things herself and took them down into Old Iacob's cellar.

I was sitting on the *calidor*, looking as much as I liked - Mother was busy. The willow trees at the edge of the common could hardly be made out because of the smoke. The smoke had become greyish-white. And it smelled, you could even smell it here. The thieving beggars under the willows were still firing, even when our airplanes weren't flying above them. In between spurring Mother on (that she shouldn't tire herself, that was men's work), Old Iacob said that the beggars even fired into the air straight ahead of them. To get rid of their ammunition so they wouldn't be weighed down when they had to flee from our boys.

From the courtyards I could see across the back lane, women were coming out with bundles, children and hens under their arms. They came into the lane, then into our yard, through our garden to reach the forest more easily, so I heard.

"We must stick t'gether, Missus, t' make things easier," I heard Maxim's wife say.

"When two o' you stick t'gether, things grow even without th' rain!" giggled Ileana, the swarthy daughter-in-law.

Duda came through our garden as well. She was only with her grandmother. Duda wasn't really little any more, now she went to dances and went to sit on the women's socials, and people said that she went to lie down with the young fellows in the vineyards and in the forest as well; but she wasn't so big that she couldn't play with me any more (the last time at our house, in the kitchen, Mother caught us and clouted me on both ears and marched Duda to the door by her pigtails - and by her pigtails threw her out, telling her that if she ever caught her around here again, she would cut

76

her pigtails off - but I went to her house, when the old folks were out on the hills and inside the house there was the right kind of darkness, smelling of rosemary, and sounds of look-up-there-cos-it's-not-right-to-see-down-there). And then another five or six of Simion Cristea's children came into the courtyard. From everything that was being said - and a lot was being said - I understood what I could. And I said:

"I'll stay with the men, to protect the houses from those thieving beggars - that's men's work."

The silly women fell about laughing. I wasn't really bothered about Maxim's wife and daughters-in-law, but look! Duda was laughing as well. And I only said it for her: so she would either admire me or say nothing. However, she laughed, still with her pigtails that Mother hadn't cut off. I wanted to cry, but Old Iacob saved me.

"An' who's goin' t' protect these women then, in th' forest? From robbers? We need a man there as well!"

Quite right. Even though the women were laughing, I let myself be led away, Mother taking one hand and Duda taking the other. I knew Duda's hand very well: firm and warm and onto-the-bare-skin and smelling of rosemary - like in the kitchen in our house, and after that at her house with the shutters closed, when she said I had to look up there, because it wasn't proper. To see. Down there, down below. Now she was squeezing me in the same way. Duda said: "Look up there!"

And I would have looked, even if she hadn't told me to, but there were too many people outside for me to not-see what else was warm apart from her hand and apart from the rosemary.

We set off after the others, towards the bottom of the garden.

"The dog!" Mother stopped us. "What are we going to do with Osman. Old Iacob, we can hardly leave him tied up here!"

Osman was snarling, he was chained around the neck but

77

was still pulling and rushing at the women and children who were going past with their backs to the fence, and he was baring his fangs. I didn't hear what Old Iacob replied to my mother, I stayed with Duda. No...I was without her for a while, she was frightened of Osman and ran away. I stayed without Mother as well, at the fence. Osman wasn't pulling any more or snarling. But his eyes were still yellow and the hair on his back was like a hedgehog's. Ever since the Russians pulled Father in last winter, the dog had never been let loose from the chain. He didn't know anybody. Osman only knew Father. Ever since Father had been pulled in by the Russians, Mother had given the dog food and drink in two metal bowls, each tied onto the end of a long pole. Osman was a wolf-hound. Everybody said that he was even more vicious than a wolf.

When Mother returned and took my hand to lead me away, Osman started yelping.

"I'll untie him, he knows me," I said.

"Do you want to be eaten alive?" Mother got frightened and with all her strength pulled me towards her, away, towards the bottom of the garden.

We crossed through a field of corn which had just been hoed. It's excellent when the cornfield has been freshly weeded and you're barefoot; if your head is hot, your feet are nice and cool. It was a pity: I was still quite small and couldn't see over the top. Mother could see, and was shouting over the top with the other women. I asked her to pick me up, so that I could see the women shouting - Duda, I mean, to see if she could see me like I could see her. Instead she jerked my hand so hard I nearly fell down - I don't understand what Mother had against that girl, against Duda.

But even if she hadn't anything against Duda's pigtails, Mother still wouldn't have been able to pick me up; she had an uncomfortable bundle over her shoulder which kept slipping, and in her hand below she had another tied-up

78

bundle. Then we started to hurry: it was still quite a way to the forest. Even if I couldn't see, I knew the area.

The roar of the guns under the willow trees sounded further away, and they had a new colour and shape now: they seemed like the great drumrolls of Volinca's music.

Something was getting closer that was crackling.

"The Rus-sians!" shrieked Maxim's Ileana.

As she'd done earlier in the house, Mother threw me to the ground and lay on top of me; and like in the house, she was crushing my nose - it wouldn't have been so bad if we'd been in the freshly hoed field, but we were in another one with dried clods of earth which were sticking in my cheek.

"Now! As fast as y'can! Before he comes back!" It was Ileana's voice again.

We picked ourselves up and ran through the corn. I didn't have time to make Mother account for why she'd thrown me on the ground and pressed my face into dried-out lumps of soil.

"The Russian's comin' back! On th' ground!" somebody shouted.

This time, I threw myself down, like a grown-up man. Mother lay at my side but still covered me with the bundle she'd been carrying in her hand. I tried to push it off me, but Mother then lay completely on top of me. In between the crackling sounds, I could hear her, at my ear, pleading, whispering about the child, the-child-has-to-be-saved; and so I didn't move. I didn't cry. I started to grow up.

Then a woman shouted that we had to run as fast as we could again. We stood up and ran for it. We reached the road, scrambled up by grabbing onto tufts of grass; and we stopped, panting, under the first lot of trees in the forest. Ileana got there before us, just look at her: she went back onto the road and even climbed the slope at the other side, towards the corn field.

"Are you mad, girl?" the women shouted. "The Russian's comin' back!"

I could spot the Russian now as well: he was coming from the right, from Orhei. The nose of the plane was rounded, and if the ears of corn had been fully grown, its twisted wheels would have brushed them. Look at the star, as well, I heard somebody say, and something else about kissing backsides. Maxim was saying things like that under his breath. One star on the side of the plane - in books they were on the wings as well, but I could only see one on the side as it flew over the corn. Mother was searching for me with her free hand, to pull me closer or to throw me down again, but I wriggled away, escaping her clutches. And I could see ab-so-lute-ly everything. I could see Ileana bending right forward and lifting her skirt right up, to the Russian. And now she was smacking something that made a slapping sound:

"Here y'are, you thievin' beggar! If you're a man, stick yer lead in here! Here it is! Down here! Here it is!"

The airplane had disappeared some time ago, to the left, but Ileana was still running about, slap-slap on her down here, which I couldn't see from where I was. The women were cheering, shrieking, laughing. I could hear the very last of their voices - Mother succeeded in grabbing my hand and pulling me away.

"What was Ileana saying she'd give to the Russian, Mother?" I asked, breathless from Mother's haste.

"Nothing, Ileana's a fool," Mother said.

"What was she asking for? What does it mean - stick your lead in, Mother? What was down here?"

"I don't know, I didn't see - now off you go by yourself, you're a big boy now."

Sure I was a big boy now. I asked Mother to give me a bundle to carry - Mother gave me her handkerchief to take for her. I threw it away and dashed back to the group of women. I went up to Ileana, took her by the hand and asked her to bend over and whispered in her ear,

"Show me your down here as well, so I can see what it's

like..."

Ileana, the fool, started to laugh and repeated out loud what I had asked her in a whisper. The women were shrieking with laughter. Mother, who was furious, grabbed me by the ear and led me, by the ear, right into the heart of the forest.

The mosquitoes were murdering us. The women covered their heads and arms with shawls and their legs with skirts that reached the ground. When we stopped anywhere, they could spread out their skirts like gypsy women, they had something to protect themselves with - but what about me? In short trousers and a short-sleeved shirt...

"Give 'im one of yer dresses, Missus, otherwise you'll 'ave t' leave 'im behind, the mosquitoes'll eat 'im alive!" Ileana said.

Mother began looking through her bundles - but I didn't want one. I did want a dress, but not one of Mother's. I wanted Ileana's dress. And I told her what I would have, if I could have anything in the world.

"But I haven't got another one, chicken, I left in such a big hurry," Ileana said. "What? An' what w'd I be left with? D'y want me to be left only with my birthday suit? Is that what y' want? Really?"

"Not yet," I said. "All I want now is that you hold me to down there. Then I'll be rid of the mosquitoes and I can see what down there's like."

I couldn't understand why Mother was so angry that day: she put a red cotton bedspread on top of my head, got hold of the corners and led me like a horse by the reins further away, somewhere else...

Onto a barren hillside.

You could have said that Mana had moved onto a barren hillside as well. No men, only women and children - onto a steep, muddy, damp and dark hillside. With clucking hens, gaggling geese, gobbling turkeys and grunting pigs. And it smelled of young wood burning. And of aromatic grasses and herbs from the forest. But more than anything, it smelled of good food which made my eyes cloud over.

And the food didn't only smell of food any more. Now it smelled of Duda. After Mother had brought me a bowl of boiled chicken from the people next to us, she told me not to move from the spot and that she was going to find something else to eat, for me. The moment Mother disappeared, Duda appeared: so I could let her come underneath as well, because of the mosquitoes. She said, wriggling under the brick-red bedspread:

"Why did you want Ileana's dress? Didn't you say that you only wanted me?"

I could remember saying that about Ileana's dress but not about only wanting Duda... Anyway, I didn't want Ileana's dress, I wanted her down there. And Duda didn't have one. And I told her so. She didn't understand.

She cuddled up next to me, but straight away she said that the mosquitoes were getting in through the sides and underneath, she said that there were too many of us for one blanket and said that there should only be one of us - because of the mosquitoes. So, at first she said that I should sit in her lap; then I should move a bit further up, and she pulled her dress up, so that it wouldn't crease. Now it was nice: it was like sitting in the armchair at home, but a much better armchair, warm, tailor-made for me, hugging all of me. Duda said that it would be even better than that if I took my trousers off; and even better again if I turned around to face the back of the chair - I said that was it, but she didn't; she said that no, that wasn't it, I had to move a bit higher or a bit lower. I said that that couldn't be it because now my back was in the cold; Duda curled one of her warm hands around my back and pulled me to her; with the other hand she undid the top of her dress and pressed my mosquito-bitten cheek to where it was warm and airy and really nice.

"Look up there, 'cause it's not right to look down

below."

I lifted my cheek away from the warmth of her up there and, keeping my eyes closed, poked my head out, above the blanket while, under the blanket, Duda was making things feel really nice, like at home in the kitchen when she was sitting on the chair, or at her house in the big room with the shutters closed, when she was sitting on the edge of the bed and saying. What she was saying. But now it seemed even much, muuuch nicer - and that was why I was really annoyed with Mother when she snatched the blanket from us, smacked Duda twice and said to her:

"You rotten girl! You're ruining my child!"

She lifted me much higher up there and took me, blanket and all, into a kind of shelter made of leaves, where there were only little children and old women.

In the shelter I was crying for a little while peacefully, then sobbing, and then heaving so much I wanted to be sick. I left the place and set out to the right: I was going to let myself be scratched by the branches and the bramble bushes, take all my clothes off so the mosquitoes would kill me, murder me, so that Mother would find me dead, dead as a doornail - then she would be sorry. Why had she bullied me about Ileana and her dress? Why had she given me a thrashing about Duda with no dress? Duda, who was so warm and said so sweetly, "Look up there"... And why was she always hitting her when she was warm and nice? And why had she called her rotten? And said that she was ruining me? How's that, when it was so nice it was nearly too nice, how could I be ruined? By the heat? Because we're made of flesh? We are, but not cut meat - look, a cow doesn't go rotten or ruined when it's live, neither does a pig or a hen, which means that we couldn't go rotten. Even if Duda is cut a little bit. Or perhaps I'd go rotten, if I looked up there? And if I looked down there I wouldn't be rotten any more? - but no, that would mean I'd annoy Duda, and then it would be cold.

But just look, I didn't die; and Mother wasn't sorry. In fact she told me off for wandering through the forest with no clothes on, even though I told her I couldn't hear because the mosquitoes had pierced my eardrums, and that I couldn't open my eyes because they'd attacked my eyelids as well.

Later I was lying on a blanket, in a little glade: it was like a kind of *calidor*, I could think about whatever I liked. The mosquitoes had gone and the sun was shining the next day and the day after. From time to time, Mother climbed down the hill to dampen the towels which had dried out, leaving me wrapped up in a wet one sprinkled with vinegar - for the mosquitoes.

I was re-a-ll-y sad. I didn't want Duda any more: instead of coming to see me when Mother went down the hill, to ask me if it hurt (it was her fault anyway that I was murdered by the mosquitoes) she was going out with the young fellows. Lying down with them. Mother was right. Duda was rotten. And not rotten like meat, but like something else. You went rotten, when you let Macarie's son Gligor ruin you - I saw it happen, yesterday. How could you not become rotten, when you're stretched out so wide, when Gligor climbs on top of you and crushes you, moaning with the pain - I saw absolutely everything: I was just lying here alone in the sun and here came Duda towards me; I thought she was coming to see me to ask me how I was, but she didn't even notice me and crossed the glade to the other side, looking behind her all the time - and who was coming behind her? Gligor! And they disappeared into the bushes. And so I got up and went after them, on all fours through the grass and then on my stomach, like soldiers do in a war. I found them not too far away and got so close that I could have touched Gligor's heels. And I saw and heard: Mother was right, Duda is really rotten - but she hadn't been when she called her a rotten girl and smacked her so that she wouldn't ruin me and make *me* rotten. With me she wasn't rotten, she went rotten when Gligor ruined her, and I saw that he was always rotten to

84

her, and I was really, really surprised afterwards that he could still walk like a man, as if he hadn't ruined her legs by spreading them out and lifting them up so high, to say nothing of when he was hitting himself against her and crushing her, there - but not just a little bit, he was moving forward all the time but his feet stayed in the same place on the ground, close together, and even though her cheeks were really red she didn't seem to be crying, she didn't even cry with the pain - after so much pain she'd endured from that swine of a Macarie's son, he had made her go rotten, the poor girl.

If she'd come to see me, if the two of us had gone into the bushes, I wouldn't have pulled a trick like that, I was fond of Duda, I would have stroked her and I would only have looked up there so that I didn't ruin her and make her rotten. It's not right to make them go rotten. But if she kept pretending that she didn't know me any more...

I was sitting near the fire in the glade. The smells coming from the metal pot were nearly as good as Duda - before she went rotten. I was waiting for the chicken broth which Aunt Domnica was saying a charm over; she'd come into the forest as well, after two nights of hell-'n'-fire she said, but then she said there hadn't been a fire in the village - only bombs and bullets. She was talking and so were the others who were still left, telling us how they'd slipped back into the village when it was dark, to get a few more things, mostly hens.

No, the Russians hadn't left the common, in fact they'd received reinforcements from Orhei, they'd even used their own deserters from the Prut. As for staying somewhere, they hadn't taken over the houses, only their big Boss who was at the school, but they were going into people's houses, taking what they could find and destroying what they didn't need - pagans! Our men were quite near. The Romanians were coming and would send them packing quickly enough - couldn't you hear the big cannon? - that was the cannon of

Cornesti - the worst part was over...

"If not today, then t'morrow!" people were saying, all of us were saying so.

"Lord above!" Maxim's wife said, "The first one o' ours I see, when I see 'im I'll fall t' me knees and kiss 'is machine gun - I've been waitin' now for aaages!"

Other women dabbed their eyes with the corners of their handkerchiefs as well. Nearly all of them. Mother was silent, her eyes were dry. Maxim's daughter-in-law, the devilish Ileana said:

"After y've bowed down to 'im, hand 'im over t' me! I'll unfasten all 'is machine guns..." and she started rubbing her hands together.

Giggles and cackles - even her mother-in-law was laughing. Covering her mouth with her hand, she said, through her handkerchief:

"But have you no shame, Ileana? If *he* 'eard you, Gheorghe..." - and she giggled.

"Let it be, sourpuss, that's what war's about! D'you think our Gheorghe, wherever 'is eyes 're shinin' now, wouldn't let 'is machine guns be unfastened? By a randy old woman like me?"

I asked Mother in a whisper:

"What's that, *randy*, Mother? Is that it, when you stand with your hands on your hips? Like Ileana's standing now?"

"Something like that," Mother said, her mouth all pursed up.

So be it. Now they were talking about the damage in the village - not only this and that but everything! Everyone was talking and forcing a laugh about the dead cow, their ruined houses, how good it was that our boys were coming, that's how it was in war - but when the war ended, everything would be put to rights again. Hilarity: a bomb had fallen on the priest's stable - when he got back from the other side of the Prut, he could make himself another, or even two, he had enough money. Another bomb had fallen on Scridon's

86

house - he intended to make himself another one as well, one out of stone with a tiled roof and a porch... Scridon's wife was really happy, it was as if the bomb had built, not destroyed her house. Some of the storehouses had been burned, but that's what war was about, and we shouldn't worry, our boys would come, if not today, then tomorrow.

However, the bullets had landed everywhere; bits of lead had come down like a landslide, some of them said, like rain, the others said. They killed Moise's cow, broke the windows in so-and-so's house in the lane, so-and-so's walls were riddled with bullets, so-and-so's chimney had been shot off - yes, oh yes, the lead had fallen all right, no joke...

Lead - I knew what lead was. We had a piece in the school museum, on the shelf with the Minerals and the Metals. Lead - how could I not know what lead was? This is what it was like - about the size of a big walnut, but the shape of a cantaloup, yes, that was it, you could see the grooves where the slices had to be cut; it had a little tail, a bit bent; it also had...it did have, but it broke off by itself, the lead I mean, I bent it back to see if it would break... So, leads were like big walnuts, with slices for you to cut, like cantaloups, and next to the tail was a little hole through which you could see that they were empty inside. It's a shame that we had to leave home so quickly and I didn't have time to look for them in the yard, just where Mother had been standing, and in the fence backing onto Old Iacob's - I could have collected them and put them, neatly, on the museum shelf. And if we hadn't been in such a hurry in the cornfield, I could have looked for the leads which had fallen from the Russian's plane. I would have seen Ileana's down here as well, when she was showing it to the thieving beggar, for him to stick his lead in - if we hadn't been in such a hurry. Who knows: Ileana might have got what she wanted: the lead. Maybe she already had some, when I asked her to show me, but she didn't want to show it to me as well. But perhaps if I asked her again nicely, perhaps she'd show it to me; perhaps she'd even give it to me - to take to the school museum, to put it on the Minerals and Metals shelf. I could ask Mother to write a label for ILEANA LEAD and I could put the IRON, PYRITE, COPPER and BRASS around it and there we'd go, enriching the museum!

But there was one thing I didn't understand: I'd held the lead from the museum, the original, and I knew that it was damned heavy, even though it was empty inside. If it was so heavy, if it fell on your head, it would have killed you - like Moise's cow. But why, when it fell on Ileana, didn't it do anything to her? Because it didn't fall on her head, that was why: if it fell on your head, you were killed, but if it stuck in down here, you weren't completely dead. I didn't think that it had even hit her - if she'd had it, the lead, she wouldn't have been asking for it all the time; and she wouldn't have stood with her hands on her lips like she did. If the lead had stuck in her down here, she wouldn't have said she was an old woman.

Three days later, Mother said:
"Good day to you all. We're going to Camincea, it's not on the front and I'll be able to find medical assistance for the boy..."

I followed Mother up the path, without feeling sorry I didn't know whether it was the front or not at Camincea, or whether we'd find the doctor's assistant - what would he do to me anyway? the swelling had gone down - but I did know that if we stayed in the forest any longer, Calistru's son Ilie would have stolen from Mother.

I'd woken up in the middle of the previous night when Mother was hitting someone with something and she didn't want to wake me up. I heard her whisper, and then she hit him with all her might; he wasn't bothered though and kept reaching out his hands to Mother, and talking about prudes, that she shouldn't be a prude, because she was a young widow - and Mother had said:

"My husband's coming back, he'll show you, trying to get your hands on me!"

But the man had just laughed - "...But until Teacher-Sir does come back from Siberia, if he ever does" - and he reached out his hands to grab her again, and you could hear her dress tear. And Mother, who was livid with anger, but still talking under her breath, said,

"You've ripped my dress, you cripple! If you get any closer, I'll break your other leg!"

Then I knew it was Calistru's son Ilie, a young fellow who was exempt. Quickly I looked for a stone to hit him on the head with, but where was I to find a stone in the forest, in the dark? And so I got hold of a piece of wood that was burning in the embers of the fire and screamed and pounced on him.

We didn't go to bed again, and stayed next to the fire until morning, Mother trembling the whole time. Around us, old women were giggling and laughing. Mother said:

"Pretend you can't hear!"

I pretended. After I'd pretended, I asked:

"What did the Cripple want? Did he want to take something from you?"

"Yes, he wanted to..." - Mother clenched her teeth. "He wanted to take my money, to rob me."

So it was better that we left, the place was full of robbers and mosquitoes.

Mother walked along the path in front of me, with the bundles. She was constantly looking back over the top of my head, or to the side. She wasn't trembling any more but I knew that she was frightened. And who by. That was why I nicked a fork out of one of the bundles before we left; I stuffed it under my belt, under my shirt. Mother was looking behind her, to the left and to the right - however, she didn't see that right in front of us waited Ilie the Exempted. He was waiting for us in a little clearing in the forest, leaning against a pile of firewood which had been neatly stacked, then white-washed - so it couldn't be stolen.

When she set eyes on him, Mother started trembling and got a tight hold on my shoulder. She said we should go back. I got the fork out and said, in my deepest voice:

"Don't be afraid, you're with me. I'll give it to him..."

And just look what happened: the cripple spat the straw out of his mouth, started whistling, walked around the back of a stack of firewood and disappeared.

But Mother still didn't want us to head on, she wanted to go back. Now it was my turn to take her firmly by the hand and pull her after me - it was just as well I'd come into the forest, to protect these women from rogues and robbers!

By the afternoon, we'd reached the other side of the forest - beyond the stubble was Camincea. We sat down on the grass to get our breath back. Mother was still looking over her shoulder, behind us.

"Don't be afraid!" I said. "He's not following us any more. You saw how frightened he was of me, didn't you?"

"I did. I did," said Mother. "When he saw me with you - did you see how he ran away?!" - and Mother started laughing out loud, really loud, and slapped me on the back and started laughing again.

I laughed as well and looked at my muscles and at the fork.

"Have you hidden it in the same place?" I asked. "You haven't sewn it up very well."

"What am I hiding, what haven't I sewn up?"

"There," I said and pointed to her dress which she'd sewn up in a hurry and with a different coloured thread. "Where he was putting his hand, last nigh..."

The back of Mother's hand hit me with the speed of lightning.

"Who's been teaching you that filth? That rotten Duda again?"

No, no Duda, and why filth? And why was she hitting me again, wasn't I the one who'd defended her, last night, with the burning wood and the fork? Sulking, I walked along behind her, on the path between the stubble fields.

I was beginning to understand: Gligor had been robbing Duda in the bushes; he lifted up her dress, made her spread out and crushed her, so he could steal her money which she'd hidden down there. But what I didn't understand was: why hadn't she defended herself like Mother did? At least if she'd appeared annoyed about the theft, but she didn't even cry. Huh! If I'd had the fork with Duda, I'd have protected her and she wouldn't have been robbed and wouldn't have gone rotten.

The apricots were falling like pieces of lead from the trees - only they were the special yellow of the fruits of Camincea. Yellow and speckled. When Madam got hold of one side of the trunk and Mother got hold of the other and the pair of them started shaking the tree, the yellow ran down, it moved, from a round ball on top down to a wide circle on the grass. There were so many yellow leads together on the green grass, that not even my bare feet could dodge through them without squashing them, and so I had to begin collecting them from the edges. Madam and Mother started from the trunk outwards.

Madam was a teacher as well. She had been a student with Mother at the teacher training school in Chisinau. Her husband had been one of Father's colleagues at the teacher training college in Orhei. Madam didn't have a husband any more either; he'd been pulled in by the Russians as well, at the same time - last winter. However, Madam had two children, girls: one was about my age, but much naughtier than I was, who was called Emilia, people called her Mili; the other one was three years older, Nora - from Eleanora. But Nora didn't benefit at all from being the older one: her sister, the naughty little devil Mili, was always hitting her, nipping her, pulling her hair, digging her in the ribs and breaking her dolls. The big sister endured everything and kept quiet - cried, that is. Nora cried more beautifully than anyone in the world. Madam was a bit taller and slimmer than Mother, and almost as beautiful; even though she had black hair and dark eyes - the little sister Mili looked like her, but Nora didn't: she had blonde hair and green eyes - like me. Nora had a bluey-green bow in her hair as well, and when she wasn't being tormented by that little brat of a sister, she played Miss High 'n' Mighty: she always walked around with a book under her arm, and if you wanted to talk to her for a little while, she didn't have time to listen - she was reading...

We were sitting down to have something to eat, outside at a table under a mulberry tree. Madam had sat Nora to her left and Mili to her right so they wouldn't be able to reach each other and there'd be some peace while we ate. Mili was quite well-behaved, but as soon as Madam turned to look the other way to do something - she started throwing the bread at her sister. Once, then twice... I told her it wasn't nice...

"And are you nice, the way you follow her around?" Mili threw back at me and stuck her tongue out at Nora.

Madam coughed, I went red. Out of shame. What did she mean, that I...and her big sister, I don't know... Then Mili pinched me on the leg, poured a glass of water over me and dug me in the ribs with her sharp elbow. Because Madam, after she'd coughed, had said something about getting out the little stick, Mili became re-a-ll-y well-behaved: she put both hands on the table and sat with her head up straight. However, under the table she'd taken off one of her shoes and was jabbing me in the legs with her toes - and kneeing me. I didn't say anything. I didn't get annoyed. Out of the corner of my eye, I looked at Nora who was sitting at the other side of Madam, and, in my thoughts, told her that her sister was a stupid little girl and that I wouldn't even entertain her, I was a man. That's what Old Iacob had said, when I'd protected Mother from Ilie the Exempted, who'd wanted to rob her, and that if it was up to me, I'd protect Nora as well, she just had to tell me what she wanted - for the time being, she didn't say anything to me, the devil of a Mili was torturing her, but not robbing her.

At the beginning, I'd shown her what big muscles I had on my arms - really huge. She stuck out her bottom lip, and made the most horrible sound, one that girls shouldn't make - especially teachers' daughters - and especially since her father had been pulled in by the Russians. Later, I'd picked a stone up and when I threw it at the sky, it didn't even come down, it stayed up there - but Nora didn't see, she had started reading. Then I said to her, "Let's have a wrestling match!" - she shrugged her shoulders and walked off, pretending to be the greatest reader ever. I let her go, remembering that only men have wrestling matches. I wanted to tell her that I knew all the letters of the alphabet, every single one - even though I'd just started school - and I knew how to write them, but reading was harder, I'd find it a tiny bit difficult.

I was picking the apricots up carefully and putting them neatly into the basket. That spitting image of the Devil, Mili, started hurling the ripest ones at me, only after she'd crushed them to a pulp with her heel. I didn't take any notice of her: she was a girl - little and stupid. And I didn't even get annoyed when she came up behind me and pushed me, and I fell head first into the basket, right into the fruit we'd picked. Madam said:

"Mili, I'll pull your ears off if you don't leave the little boy alone!"

I felt like throwing a really well squashed apricot right at Madam - what did she mean, little boy?

"It's nothing," I said, in my deepest voice. "She's so small..."

"But you're tiny as well, like your mama!"

Madam swept Mili up (I knew the method, from Mother)

and carried her under her arm into the house - a few *I-won't-do-it-agains* came through the window.

"Don't you talk like Mili, you're a big boy," Mother said to me. "Otherwise I'll..."

I knew - how could I not have known? Madam came back and said,

"Right, the picking's over for today. Off you all go! Go and play!"

She said, you all go, but she looked only at me when she said it. I didn't like that. She was sending only me - all of me - to play, but not the girls. They were allowed to sit and listen when she was talking to Mother. Sometimes Madam would cry and Mother would put her arm round her waist and tell her that the-Lord-was-Good-and-he'll-come-back; other times when Mother was crying Madam would put her arm round her shoulder and stroke her hair and say that the-Lord-was-Good-he'll-come-back. This was what the women were doing nearly all night, on the gallery, I could hear them through the open window.

I really would have liked to talk to Nora. About our fathers. She could have cried, and I could have stroked her, her hair, her little bow, and wiped away her tears and said, in the deepest-ever voice, it's all right, the Lord's-Good... Then I could have been sad and she would have stroked me, and told me that the-Lord's-Good. But I couldn't, there was too much light and we weren't on the gallery.

I took one of the baskets full of the apricots we'd picked and went up to the blanket Nora was sitting reading on. I asked her really nicely if she wanted me to give her the nicest one of all the apricots - look, it was this one; even these two, the two which were the prettiest yellow and with the best blood-coloured speckles.

But she, without even lifting her bow out of the book said:

"If I want one, I'll take one myself! They're ours anyway!"

Of course they were theirs. I didn't say they were mine, I just asked nicely if she wanted some apricots - because I was fond of her. Even if she pretended to be the greatest reader ever.

I wanted to cry. Like a baby. But I controlled myself. I put the two apricots down on the corner of the blanket and went off. Where? Into the house - their house. I mean her house. If I stayed in the orchard - that was hers as well. The yard and the house and the apricots - everything was.

Mother was still busy crying with Madam and with the-Lord's-Good. She didn't have time for me - even when the little pest was nipping me and digging her elbows in me, and even now, when Cleverclogs told me that they were hers and she was reading!

And so I decided to go off into the wide wide world. Byebye everyone, I'm going into the forest. So that Ilie the Cripple would rob me, so the mosquitoes would finish me off; so the wolves would swallow me up whole; or so I could get into a war and be hit by a piece of lead and be butchered alive!

I went out into their yard; then into the back lane - theirs as well, but I didn't hesitate, I went straight to the left, to the other lane which turned into a little path - the one we'd walked along when we came from the forest. My feet were dripping with the dust, which was at least a foot deep, and I was crying. I felt so sorry for myself. I was crying, but not out loud; in case someone saw me and thought I was a little boy. I walked straight through the middle of the stubble fields, so I could get more quickly to where I was going to die.

Somebody was shouting behind me. Shouting out my name. Her bluey-green ribbon - what did she want now? To tell me that the stubble field was hers as well? Or in any case, it wasn't mine? She was calling to me to stop and wait for her. That she couldn't go any faster; she'd been running for ages and her feet were really sore. She was shouting that I had to stop, couldn't I hear? Because she was an orphan, the Russians had pulled her dad in - as if it had only happened to her dad. Couldn't I wait just for a little bit, she had something to tell me. Something very important.

I didn't answer and didn't stop, although I did slow down. I kept on my way, barefoot, through the stubble field. Without turning around, I told her that if she wanted me to stop, then she had to take her shoes off as well. Otherwise I wouldn't.

I wouldn't have listened if I'd been her. Just look at how she was walking along now - like a stork. I stopped and explained to her how you had to walk in a stubble field when you had no shoes on: you didn't put your foot straight down, you had to push your heel in first, ssshhh, and then put your foot down - that was how, if you didn't want to get pricked.

I reached the forest. She was way behind me, sandals in hand, treading the ground as if she were crossing a stile, stone by stone; or as if she were jumping right over the stile and still getting pricked - she deserved it. She might have been older than me, but if she didn't know how to walk through a stubble field, she didn't know what life was all about. To show her just how little I was bothered about her thick books and yellow apricots, I went into the forest without even looking behind me. She was shouting for me, trying to find me. I wasn't hiding. I was just keeping going.

So she could run and catch me up, she'd put her sandals on again. She caught up with me and sat down in front of me. There were streams of tears mixed with dust down her cheeks. She said that I had to go back home. She said that she wanted to go home but she was frightened to go back alone and said that big boys were supposed to accompany little girls home. She said that even if she was older than I was, I was a big boy and was strong, not like her, a little girl. And so big boys had to do what they were asked by little, sad, orphan girls. When she saw that I was looking at her, she said she'd give me her middle doll; and then the big book she had just been reading. What did I mean, which big book? The *magnum opus*. She didn't know what that was, but that's what her mother had said, that it was something very great, from an opera. What did I mean, I didn't want the doll or the *magnum opus*? What did I want then?

"I want to die! I'm going into the forest and the Russians will come and eat me alive - and that's the end of it!"

She started crying, because she didn't want to be eaten alive. Because she was an orphan and wanted to go home, to her mama.

"And to your apricots!" I said.

She pretended not to know what I was talking about: what about the apricots?

I walked around her and walked further into the forest. After a little while, I came to a clearing. It wasn't very big, only big enough for the two of us. I sat down and pulled a thorn out of my heel. She sat down as well, in front of me. I didn't really have a thorn in my heel, I know how to walk in a stubble field, but I told her I had. After I'd put another, real thorn in my mouth, I sucked my foot, then took the thorn out of my mouth and showed it to her.

She was like putty in my hands after the thorn! She didn't pretend to be reading any more - she was looking at me with her mouth open, her bow was pert and I had all her attention. After I'd devastated her with the thorn, I told her to astonish me with something. For example, putting her foot in her mouth. She could lift it up quite a bit, but not right up; she had her sandals on. I told her why. She took them off, and now she could do it, but why had she bothered? She didn't have a thorn in her heel - like I had found in mine. She put her finger out to see how sharp it was and shook her head, mine was really big and sharp, then looked again to see if she could find one: sucked and sucked - nothing. But she did have another little bow which was making me go weak at the knees - but I didn't tell her.

I had to find something else. I suggested that we have a **running competition - she said that girls didn't have running** competitions with boys; well, couldn't we see who could climb up the oak tree the fastest? - she said that girls didn't go up trees. I asked her why. She said:

"So that the boys don't see their little birdy."

I knew what a girl's little birdy was like, I'd seen plenty of them, in Mana. I told her that you couldn't see hers because she had panties on, I'd seen them.

"But if I climb up the tree you'll see it!" she said.

"I won't see it," I said. "We'll have an experiment: you go up and you'll see that I can't see it! At all, at all!"

She lay down, resting on her elbow, in the grass. She was looking up at me from underneath her eyelashes:

"If I don't show you it, you can't see it - but if I show you mine, will you show me yours as well?"

I suggested that we should have a competition at something good - she said that boys only had competitions with boys and that girls didn't have competitions with boys. I asked her: so what did girls do with boys?

"They lie down," she replied.

I told her that that's what they might do, but you couldn't have lying-down competitions. She said of course you could, you could, she knew how - didn't I want her to show me? I sighed and said it would be better if we had a competition in something interesting, not in lying down, in something really interesting - running, throwing, climbing; or at spitting - let's see: who could spit the furthest? I did a trial one for her to see, but she pulled a face and said it was horrid. Well, weeing then - who could wee the longest and the highest? She said that was even more horrid. It would be better if we lay down. I asked her what we were doing now, weren't we lying down?

"Not like grown-ups," she said. "Do you want me to show you how grown-ups lie down?"

She lay on her back on the grass, lifted up her little dress and opened her legs. She said we'd pretend she was the girl and that I was the boy; and let's say that the boy lies down to go to sleep on top of the girl - that's what it meant when a girl slept with a boy.

I told her that when you went to sleep you didn't lie like that and that when you did lie like that, you made the girl rotten and ruined her. She pulled her panties to the side and showed me:

"It doesn't get ruined. There's nothing to get ruined on girls."

"But there is, I know! I've ruined one, but it was bigger," and I showed her how big.

"It was bigger, huh? I haven't got a big one or a little one, girls don't have one, they cut it off so we can be girls."

"Su-per-sti-tions!" I said. "You can't chop the little prick off because it hurts - do you remember it hurting?"

"No...I was only little."

She leaned right forward, looked and looked, trying to find it:

"What did I tell you: there isn't one! Girls haven't got one."

"Who's going to believe you?" I said, looking in the other direction. "I didn't see what you showed me, you didn't let me - God knows what you might have down there. When I ruined the big girls in Mana,...well, it was like this!" And I showed her how big.

"As big as that? And what did the girls do with all that?"

"Lots and lots of children, that's what, but when it gets even bigger, this big...when it's like that, it's only good for making them rotten... When I think of how many I've ruined..."

She was putty in my hands again. She got up, came over to me and took me by the hand:

"Will you show me how? If you show me, I'll never say anything about the apricots again. And after you've shown me how you made them rotten, I'll show you how I lay down with a boy - but he was muuuuch older than you."

I didn't want to. I was fond of her and didn't want to

99

make her rotten - and she didn't have anything to be ruined with - but I didn't tell her that, I just said that we couldn't, period. She said why couldn't we, since it wasn't like that and whether they were big or small they didn't make people rotten. I said that we weren't at home, in the kitchen on the chair, or where the mosquitoes were, or in the armchair. She said so what, we'd pretend. Then I said we couldn't, she had panties on and I had trousers on and I was ashamed to get undressed in front of a little girl. She told me to close my eyes and I would see what she was like with - and without. I closed my eyes and then I really saw it. But she didn't see mine. I tried to sit down, like under the blanket with Duda. It didn't work, Nora was too little, she didn't have any little tits yet. Then she said, "Let me show you how I lay down with a big boy!" And she said: "I have to lie on my back, I'm the girl. And the boy puts his little birdy on my little tummy button, that's how you lie down."

I put my little birdy on her little tummy button.

When we got back, Madam said:

"But where have you been, the pair of you, all this time?"

"In the forest, lying down," Nora answered proudly, holding my hand tight with one of hers, and dusting off the back of her dress with the other.

The Romanians Have Come!

A peasant house, in the courtyard, at sunset. They've separated me from Nora. We're not staying at Madam's any more, because of us lying down.

I was sleeping. I had fallen asleep in the afternoon. I was woken up by the sound of shouts, then gunshots, then shouts again which turned into cries of joy, like at a wedding - and then shots again. Trembling from the cold of sleep even though it was warm outside, I went down into the deserted courtyard. Where were our landlords? And where on earth was Mother?

I crossed the courtyard through the long grass, refreshingly cool in the shade of twilight, and passed by a little cart from which the horses had been untied and which stood resting as if on its shoulders, the shafts pointing up into the sky, like two of the cannons under the willow trees in Mana. I dodged around a haystack which was quite plump and had a good smell. And stopped. Right in front of me: the gate wide open. And in the back lane: the flag.

Neither in childhood nor in adolescence (still less in maturity) have I ever been able to reconcile myself to "parades", as Father used to call those symbols of festivity: emblems, banners, flags. The flag in particular always provoked in me a feeling of compulsory yet sad celebration...as for the flags of other countries, they never seemed to be in their right place unless they were on ships (and even then I'd only seen two or three, and only on the Danube...). I could somehow come to terms with the *essentiality* of the Japanese flag, and the Swiss one and, on condition that the lateral red stripes disappeared, the Canadian flag as well. Our Romanian tricolour has always seemed badly co-ordinated to me - blue/yellow/red - the blue being next to the yellow produces a fourth colour, green, which is too much. Moreover, since the old flag - on which there was already too much - was replaced by the Communists, who had a painting made (on the flag) of a "countryside"... The only country in the world which doesn't know what its symbol stands for and what it could, one day, be used for ...

And yet ... nevertheless ... on that summer day, late in the afternoon, it seemed like there were different colours, differently arranged on the Romanian tricolour which has remained so deeply imprinted in my memory and which will never be erased (even if it did have the blue next to the yellow...)

Strange: I didn't see (or I forgot about it and nobody bothered to tell me about it later) whether the flag was on a tank, on a gun carriage, on a little cart or carried by a cavalryman. Only the image of the flag has remained. As if it had arrived on its own and helped itself up on its own, at a constant distance from the ground. And it has remained embedded in my mind, blowing in the wind with the sun behind it, as in a photograph. In colour: the wooden shaft - whitish; at the top - a golden eagle; then the colours of the flag itself - and what else but? ...blue, then yellow, then red - but different, differently, only as I perceived them. All these elements - but only those then - said: OUR BOYS HAVE COME! THE ROMANIANS HAVE COME!

The flag, fixed in my mind, forever flying in the wind, was squarely superimposed over the other images - also static - the khaki uniforms (the Romanian khaki, a nice golden-yellow), covered in sweat and stains; the horses' mouths, covered in white foam; their bellies, wet and darker in colour; and in particular (is it possible that an olfactory sensation can remain static? why not?): the sharp smell of a worked horse, of leather bridles. And a more pungent smell, of manure - a certain kind of manure, only of *those* horses.

I went out into the back lane. I couldn't see any further up than my own height: I couldn't even see as far as the saddles, never mind the faces of the cavalrymen. In between the women surrounding *it* I could see the horses' mouths, their shaking legs, their wet bellies. And the manure, heralding their arrival. And then I could see a boot, a stirrup - a dusty boot, with darker stains on it, but still whitish in colour: obviously froth that had dripped down from the horse's mouth. And the smell: wet bridles, manure, coming ahead of it all, like a standard.

And I saw: a woman with a yellowish head-kerchief bowing down, then leaning forward to take hold of the boot with both hands to kiss it. And the smell. Then the woman withdrew with a movement she'd learned well at church, like the move of a knight on a chessboard, or after one has bowed down to the sacred icons - to make room for the others following her, but not so as to step blindly back into the path of others coming forward - and the horse manure, like a banner.

Fires - two of them. In the courtyard two roaring fires were burning under huge cast-iron pots, on tripods. The women were running about excitedly around them, checking the level of the flames, stirring the pots, then running to the house, to the back lane, back from the lane, from one fire to the other, all talking at the same time, constantly adjusting their head-kerchiefs which were always slipping down - it seemed like they had been specially bought and worn for this unique occasion - chirping like hens, or instead of the hens, which weren't clucking any more, but were boiling in the pots.

Mother was among the women who were standing at one side or another of a long table plucking the hens which had been scalded in the summer kitchen nearby. Women were running to and fro, one after the other, bringing hens which had already been cut up into pieces. Wagon ladders had been laid horizontally across a little cart and the hens were cleaned and cut up there - the pieces were collected in willow troughs.

Some of the women started singing. Then nearly all of them were singing. Mother's voice was clearly distinguishable, like a poppy seed in a sack of grain. I started singing as well, even though I didn't know the words, or the tune. Even though I was hungry.

Two older boys came running into the courtyard in a great hurry, each of them carrying two empty pails which were rattling against the wooden yokes on their shoulders. A fat woman - our landlady - scooped into the pot with a huge ladle and put the contents into the buckets:

"Quick as you can to the school, so's it don't get cold! The poor soldiers need their food hot, poor dears, it's such a time since they crossed the Prut..."

"Don't worry 'bout that, they've stopped over every night in a village to eat with the good folk," said a skinny woman.

"They might've," the landlady said, "but this chicken broth o' ours ... An' why don't we cook two or three ovenfuls of pies? Our boys only come once, t' rid us of the pagans!"

A group of women left the hens, and ran over to the neighbouring households to cook the pies.

"That's the spirit, m' dears, let's have the poor soldiers really enjoyin' themselves!"

The landlady put a piece of rabbit and two gizzards into a clay bowl and gave them to me. And a boiled carrot. I made for the shade, so I could throw the carrot away.

And then along came Madam, with the girls! She'd come prepared: wearing her little white apron and a white bonnet on her head. If we'd been at home, in Mana, Mother would have dressed like that as well. But we weren't. She was plucking the hens, and that was done without white aprons and bonnets. The little brat Mili had her task cut out with the feathers: she collected them, made them into a pile, collected more - then scattered them all around. I could see Madam flying at her, but I couldn't hear what she was saying.

Nora was pretending to help: she took one of the plucked hens and carried it over to the little cart where only one woman was left working - cutting them, gutting them, washing them with cascades of water. I picked up half of the carrot I'd thrown away and hurled it at Nora. The carrot landed in a basin of water, luckily at the time the woman had her back turned. Nora turned around slowly in my direction and saw me. She'd been waiting to see me ... But she didn't come over straight away. She wandered about around the cast-iron pots, then took a very roundabout way of eventually ending up next to me, and whispered that I should come with her. I put the basin down in the long grass and followed her.

Nora would only pay me attention these days under the fence, in the shadows, and so she went out into the back lane. At the gate, she took me by the hand.

"Where are we going?" I asked, thrilled by the touch of her hand.

"To the school. So I can show you something."

This time she was the leader. And she led like a boy. We ran along at a trot, hand-in-hand, past little carts, horses, soldiers lying down, the smell of sweat and of horse manure - a different kind with a different smell - and in between cannons which smelled of hot iron, even though it was night-time now and I hadn't heard the sound of any guns nearby. The moon had come out so we could see as we arrived at the school.

We reached the school, but we didn't go in through the gate. Nora pulled me towards a hole in the fence. At the other side were some canvas tents, with lights on inside.

And suddenly, there was another, unknown smell. Still of the-Romanians-are-coming, but it wasn't the smell of horses.

"What's that smell, what is it?" I asked Nora, in a whisper.

"Come and see."

On all fours, we moved closer to a large tent with the curtains drawn to one side. We could see some people dressed in white inside. I didn't know what they were doing to the people lying down - who were moaning and groaning.

"What are they doing, are they hitting them?" I asked.

"No, they're doctors taking care of the wounded."

"Doctors take care of the wounded, they don't hit them."

"You're only little and you don't know - come on!"

All of a sudden I was little, little, and didn't know anything. I wanted to see the wounded people, Nora pulled me further away. Under an apricot tree. One of their apricots, one of hers. But there was something else that didn't belong to her there: like logs, covered with something, like a dark canvas.

"I know what's in there!" I said, starting to tremble. "Dead people..."

"They're not dead," Nora said, and sat down, pulling me down with her. "They live forever, that's what I was told by the great officer, General Antonescu (leader of the Iron Guard). That's what he said - he said so, he told me: They are heroes! They never die, ever, they're eternal!"

"You mean, they've gone to sleep? But what if they wake up? I want to go home!"

"Don't you want to see them? I've seen them, in the light."

"No, I don't want to, I'm scared. Let's go home!"

I wanted to get away by myself, but because Nora was still holding me tightly by the hand, I dragged her away with me. First at a walk, then at a trot - then at a gallop. We got out into the back lane.

"It doesn't smell any more," I said, relieved. "Is that what they really smell like? Heroes?"

Nora nodded her head, yes, that was what heroes smelled like.

"When I become a hero, I won't smell as vile as that!" I

said.

"Then you won't be a hero, will you," said Nora. "You'll never live forever!"

"Yes I will", I said. "But I'll put some of Mother's perfume on first."

We stopped on a hillside, with the sun behind us. Here, on the hill, it was like a *calidor*: from here, you could see the village as if it were lying in the palm of your hand - Mana, our Mana...

I don't know how long we must have been away. Whatever, those of us who still had houses returned to them.

"Look, Mother, look how many balls of smoke have grown!"

They had grown and were always growing. As opposed to green trees, these whitish trees grew taller and fatter and then grew even taller again - until they reached the sky. Some of the smoke balls were growing out of the chimneys of the houses but most of them were sprouting in the courtyards and in the gardens. I liked the smoke balls. I heard somebody say - perhaps it was even Old Iacob - that a village without smoke is a dead village. Well, there you go, our Mana wasn't dead!

"Look, Mother, look, the fences have gone to sleep!"

Mother laughed. The other Manians who'd returned home laughed as well. A man slapped the ground so hard with his hat it went: Boom! - even louder than the cannon did.

"That's it, me lad! They've gone to sleep. Not one of 'em's still standin', not even part of one of 'em!"

Our Manian seemed happy enough, even though he must have noticed that his fence had gone to sleep as well. From up here, from our view of the village, the wattle fences which had gone to sleep looked like doormats spread out across the ground, especially along the back lane. Civilians and soldiers, wagons and soldiers, cannons and soldiers and portable army kitchens were entering (in a manner of speaking) or leaving (in another manner...) the yards and gardens, wiping their feet on the fence-doormats.

We went down into the village. The school fence was still standing - the one bordering on the back lane, because it was made of stone, as were the gate posts. The gate was in one piece as well, but it was wide open. The courtyard was teeming with soldiers, the windows were broken, the walls riddled with bullets, eaten away - but the school was in one piece.

"Just as well it didn't catch fire - what with those reeds...," Mother said. "Just as well we're home again."

We were home again and there was nothing wrong with the roof made of reeds. And even if there had been(and there was: in the course of the next year or two, bucketfuls of bullets were discovered in it), you couldn't tell.

We couldn't get into our own house. I mean, you could, but there were too many knee boots and ankle boots and slivers of glass. It was dangerous to venture any further forward than the *calidor* in your bare feet. The sandals I'd worn when we went away were too small for me now, although it seemed like only yesterday when we were leaving through the garden.

Old Iacob called us around to their house. Aunt Domnica had left the forest before we did; their house still looked like a house, like before. Apart from the wall where the caravanserai used to be; apart from the entrance to the cellar which they found down below, inside it; apart from other things...

Whenever there was a devil-of-a-party above ground, Old Iacob took shelter in the cellar underground. Bullets and bombs had fallen on top of the house (luckily the bombs fell in the garden, and didn't do any damage). The bullets had lodged in the door to the cellar and in the main door of the house, and luckily the entrances were on a steep incline and so everything (I mean, all of them) ended up down in his vault.

And what of our things left in the house? Well, Missus, you have to realise how things were; first and foremost the Russians stayed here, and following their usual habits they left behind a trail of destruction; and after that, this is how things were: the Russians ran off and what they didn't take with them, they broke, smashed or chucked on their way. And after that, Missus, this is what the situation was - there was nobody there for a time, they were fighting up above the village, with bombs, the Russians over there and our lads over here - yes, like wartime. And after that, Missus, it so happened that God granted that our lads, the Romanians came...

How could you possibly let yourself get annoyed with our boys - if that was how things had been?

"Don't worry yerself, Missus, just as well our lads 'ave come, things'll take care o' themselves an' it'll be better than it used t' be!" Old Iacob said, by way of conclusion.

Mother didn't say anything. She didn't seem angry. Well, only a bit about the gramophone (I found it broken at the bottom of the garden, hidden under broken records), and a bit more annoyed again about Father's wrist watch - it was her fault for leaving it at home when we left for the forest, she should have taken it with her, it wasn't that heavy...

Mother wasn't very annoyed and, to be even less annoyed, she went to help Aunt Domnica cook "something fit for the gods", for "the poor soldiers" - that's what Aunt Domnica called them as well, I think she'd picked it up from the women at Camincea. For the poor soldiers, she was going to make chicken in white sauce, cheese pies and fish pies (Old Iacob had made a flying dash up to the dams at the monastery and had come back with a sackful) ...

In our winter kitchen the big pots were bubbling on the stove; in the summer kitchen, in the iron pots which we used for boiling up the food for the pigs were now boiling both our neighbours' hens as well as our own - how could you get

109

annoyed with the poor soldiers? At the crossroads beside the wall of the old Court, three or four of their portable kitchens-on-wheels were puffing out smoke in the shape of trees. There were another three or so on the common.

The poor soldiers around our way were really kind: they gave me gizzards and chicken broth out of the cauldrons, they gave me jam out of our jars, they put me on their knees and asked me how old I was and what I was called, because they had, back home, a boy who looked just like me - even though, sometimes, his name was different.

The really brilliant poor soldiers were the ones in the garden. They had little plates on their ears and played with buttons on a wonderful cupboard made all of iron, out of which a long, thin pole grew, made of iron as well. They were brilliant because they could speak to each other miles and miles away. They talked to other soldiers - whom you couldn't even see - because they were so far away...

"Hornbeam here, this is Hornbeam - can you hear me, Sycamore?" my poor soldier called.

Hornbeam put me on his knee and put the phones on my ears. I couldn't hear anything but crackles. I asked Hornbeam to ask Sycamore if he'd seen my father.

"Hornbeam here - do you read me, Sycamore? I've got a little fellow here with me whose father was pulled in by the Russians - have you set him free by any chance? Well, he's like all of them, man, like a father: strong, handsome, good... OK then, Sycamore, if you find out anything, you'll keep me up to date."

"Sycamore said not yet - you know, my boy, what he means by 'not yet'?"

"I know," I said. "It means: 'If not today, then tomorrow .' "

I jumped off Hornbeam's knee and ran to pass on the good news: that Father was coming home, "If not today, then tomorrow" - that's what he had told me, personally, and also, Hornbeam had told Sycamore to search for and find Father, who was good and handsome and strong - like a father.

Mother came into the garden. Old Iacob came and Aunt Domnica and Old Andrei with his wife (but not Duda). A little soldier who was taller in rank and whose head was bound up in white said something to Mother in a whisper. He was standing with his back to me and shrugging his shoulders from time to time. As if he didn't know. Mother walked away with her handkerchief at the corner of her eye. Aunt Domnica was running around her, taking hold of her by the left elbow, then by the right - and then both of them went off to see to the chicken in white sauce and the pies. Old Andrei, with his hat in his hand:

"That lad with 'is trees has got t' keep tryin', Officer. With God's help 'e'll find Teacher-Sir, th' poor..."

"We'll try, old man, we'll try," the officer said, making a sign to Hornbeam to keep going.

He went off towards the house, holding the white bandages to his head, to his left and right were the two old men: Andrei and Iacob. I followed them, but Old Iacob turned around:

"You stay wi' that lad over there. When 'e finds Teacher-Sir, come runnin' as quick as you can 'n' let us 'ave th' news!"

I stayed. Only now, Sycamore said that he couldn't find Father and so our Hornbeam told Oak to look for him. And Ash. And Maple. And Elm and Hazel and...

It had become dark and a little bit cold. Mother came first with the chicken in sauce, then with the pies, then with the brick-coloured blanket to wrap me up in, so I wouldn't be cold.

I sat on top of one of their boxes, muffled up in the blanket, listening to Beech (Hornbeam was sleeping on another box nearby, talking, without his earphones on, to his mother). And I could see Father: strong, handsome, good - wandering through a dark forest full of bad trees with no

111

names - but I knew that he wouldn't be lost for a long time, only until if-not-today-then-tomorrow, because I knew, all the poor soldiers had told me, me personally, that all the good trees with nice names had set off in search of him, with Hornbeam as their leader, on horseback, telling his mother what it was like in the war and how he, personally, had found the father of a boy only a little bit younger and smaller than he was. I could see Hornbeam's boot pointing towards me, dusty and with dark stains made by the foam from the horse's mouth, and above him - fixed - the blue. The yellow. The red - and, if not today, then tomorrow.

The Romanians Have Gone

Tomorrow, however, the garden was empty, the courtyard was empty. The village was empty. I woke up late and not in our garden, but in Old Iacob's. I went out into the courtyard and over to our house, looked around the school and the garden - nobody. I started to cry, to howl. Where were the soldiers? Where was Hornbeam?

Mother said: "They've moved further on, they've got things to do, they're fighting..."

I wasn't comforted by their fighting. I wanted Father.

"But you know, they'll do that when they're fightin', my littl' lad," Old Iacob explained to me. "Yesterday, they were lookin' for us - for you, for Missus, for me an' they found us... Today, they're lookin' for th' folk in th' villages farther up there - an' they'll find 'em. Th' day after t'morrow, wi' God's grace, they'll find Teacher-Sir as well..."

"But yesterday, why did they say, if not today then tomorrow?" I cried.

"Yesterday! Yesterday's over an' done with!" Old Iacob said. "Today is today, that's why we say: If not today, then t'morrow! - That's what we say, today..."

"And what do we say tomorrow then, Old Iacob?"

"T'morrow? T'morrow we say th' same thing: If not today, then t'morrow! An' we keep on like that till we get there! God's good, you know. He'll help us t' get there."

I didn't really understand where we had to get to, but that's what Old Iacob said we had to do. And I didn't have anything else to do anyway. So, every morning I said, "If not today, then t'morrow!"

And I waited. I waited with Osman.

As soon as the soldiers left, the dog appeared. Dragging

the chain he'd pulled out of the ground. When the people in the village saw that he was free, they ran away and hid themselves wherever they could - they knew what he was like. Osman, however, came straight to our house, into the courtyard. Mother made a rush to pull me out of his path but there wasn't time: the dog pounced at us ... and yelping pitifully, lay down at our feet.

When we'd gone into the forest, we'd left the dog on his chain - who would have gone near him? After a good number of bullets and bombs had been dropped, Old Iacob realised that Osman had disappeared, chain and all. He thought he was dead, had been shot, or had choked on his chain in some bushes. But there he was: he didn't snarl any more, he didn't bare his teeth any more, he didn't lunge at people any more. Now he yelped and fawned and beat the ground with his tail, even in front of strangers. Mother unfastened his chain and left him with only his collar on. Osman, the dog who used to be a wolf, had become what we called a doormat dog. Even though he didn't lie on other people's doormats. But he didn't bark any more. I never ever heard him bark again.

Today became tomorrow, another today became another tomorrow, the fighting had moved further afield, the roar of the cannon became fainter and fainter, moving further to the east. People were always talking about the Dniester, the Dniester, the Dniester.

I sat on the *calidor*, with Osman lying at my feet. I waited.

I waited for Father to come - t'morrow, if not today; I waited for Mother to come home - tired, dusty, her eyelids red and sore, breathing through her mouth and dragging her head-kerchief through the dust in the back lane. I knew where she'd been and what she'd been doing, I'd come back from the same place only a little while before her, but pretended I'd been sitting on the *calidor* for a lifetime. I knew, that's why I didn't say anything. I left her to get washed, to change her clothes, to scrub really hard the ones she'd been wearing - especially her head-kerchief. And to put on lots of perfume. One day, she stopped putting perfume on. I asked her why, was it because she didn't have any left?

"No. No, even the perfume seems to smell of..." She didn't say what, but I knew anyway.

If you went out to the edge of the village, towards Orhei...

I hadn't seen them lying there, but I'd seen them being taken there, carried there. And more than anything I'd smelled them - if you smelled nice, like me, you didn't need to see anything, did you? And in fact you didn't even need to smell nice in times like these, and especially since it was summer. Two by two, about ten young men preparing for military service carried the stretchers. Army stretchers that they'd left behind. I didn't know which "they", but in any case, their stretchers. The young man in front walked normally; the one at the back either had a head-kerchief covering his mouth - like the women - or turned his head away as far to the side as he could, the edges of his mouth stretched and tight. Because it was summer, Old Iacob had explained to me. If it had been winter, or spring or even autumn, they wouldn't have swelled up with the heat, so that the buttons popped and the cheeks burst onto the chests - that's what I heard.

After the poor soldiers left the village, Mother had to go out onto the hills, mostly towards Orhei, around the school catchment area. That's where the big party had been, the devil-of-a-party, as Old Iacob used to say. And, because it was summer, not autumn - to say nothing of winter, which was the best time - although the best thing would have been if it had never happened at all. Mother went out to bring them in, with about ten young lads who would only go on one condition: only *our* boys. I don't know what Mother had replied at the beginning, but whatever she said, after they'd brought in all of *our* boys and laid them by Heroes' Cross, at the right side of the church in the cemetery, Mother said:

"Right. And what are we going to do with the others? Just leave them like that, on the field? Aren't they dead as well, weren't they once people?"

"They might have been, but with different traditions, how can we put pagans into our cemetery, Missus?"

"How do you know they were pagans?" Mother answered angrily. "Did you know them when they were alive? Did you ever call them to church and they refused to come?"

"What church? It was closed - they closed it, the pagans closed it for us - and you expect us to bury them with all due respect?"

"Pagans or not, we can't leave them out on the field!" Mother said. "It's not healthy for us, for the health of the people still alive - we have to bring them in and bury them!"

While this discussion was taking place, I was hiding in the lilac bushes with the boys. The cemetery bushes. I saw that Mother had taken out her silk kerchief and was waving it in front of her like you do when you want the flies or the mosquitoes to go away. But there weren't any flies or mosquitoes - it was the smell. So I nipped back home, around the back of the church where my little brother Peter's grave was. When Mother came home, I was sitting on the *calidor*. They brought the others in as well. They buried them outside the cemetery fence. On the common.

From the very first day, I hid with the boys in the lilac bushes: so we could see. We children weren't allowed to - and that was exactly why we went there, to see what was happening.

The older men dug the graves. But they ran off as the stretchers came closer. Mother got annoyed, told them off, cried - and half-crying, half-telling them off, pulled them out from where they'd been hiding and forced them back to bury the dead. Mostly out of pity for Mother, people worked with flying speed: they turned them into the graves, and then worked their spades more quickly than the eye could move

116

and covered them over even more quickly - so they didn't stink. When they'd finished, they all went off in different directions, some of them soothing their throats with water, the others with brandy.

Every time she came home, in between one "trip" and another, to get washed and changed ... and to put on some perfume, Mother gave Old Iacob a good dressing-down. Instead of making himself scarce like a man, when he saw Mother he'd come out to meet her like a fool, and say:

"But you shouldn't 've, Missus, that's men's work!..."

You should have heard what Mother said to him! That he was good for nothing, neither as a mayor, nor as a man - that he, as the mayor and as a man, should have taken care of it and not left her, a woman to... Old Iacob lowered his voice, bent his back, started to limp, grabbed hold of his stomach and whined that he would have done it, and have put all his heart into it, but he was re-a-ll-y ill, that he had pains here "in the heart" - and, with his fist clenched, pressed his stomach...

"You're ill and I'm the prime minister - you're a good-for-nothing, that's all you are!" Mother shouted. "Just wait, the Romanians are on their way, I'll tell them down at Orhei just how you've performed your duties as mayor! Just wait until my husband comes back, I'll tell him just how you looked after a poor, defenceless woman!"

Old Iacob stepped backwards out of sight, saying that as far as his duties were concerned, he did them: he "took care" of them! In fact, he was "takin' care" of the most difficult things, and the most dangerous: bringing in the weapons and ammunition; and if Missus wanted to exchange jobs he'd renounce what he was taking care of, with all his heart, and *he* would go out after the dead - "they at least didn't bite any more" - and we'd see whether a woman, even if she was a lady, had the attributes to get involved in *real* men's work, if she could handle it - she couldn't! Because weapons and ammunition had to be handled - because "those things could bite!" He, as mayor and as a man, had the necessary attributes to bring them into his house, into the caravanserai, to collect anything that could go Boom! while Missus, if she didn't mind him saying so, didn't know how to handle them, she hadn't done any military service...

The man in Old Iacob was lying through his teeth: even though people might bring him (held between two fingers, their arms stretched out in front of them, walking on tiptoes, their eyes popping out of their heads and their mouths wide open) a pistol, a gun, or a handful of cartridges (heavy weapons had to be "marked" and referred to Orhei - but without being touched) and he gave them a lengthy explanation of "the instructions for use, when you handled them" - he had not done any military service. Neither under the Romanians - let's say he was a bit too old - nor under the Russians. He hadn't done it because he was exempted. Exempt as "disabled". Sound as a bell, only that the very index finger on his very right hand, I mean, the very one which would have had to pull the trigger, was ... crooked.

I think at least half the men of his age in Mana were exempt - and all because of the very same damned index finger on their right hand! At that time - I mean, under the Russians - an exemptor, by trade, lived in one of the neighbouring villages, who, for so many roubles, would chop off the very index finger you had to use to shoot at the enemy; for so many more roubles, he'd chop your hand off - the right one of course; however, for a few roubles more, he'd shoot you in the index finger with a pistol and really make it crooked, by strapping it over the middle finger and tying it to your palm over a stick, so it would mend that way, really crooked ... Like Old Iacob's...

The cannons could hardly be heard any more, Mother had finished her "trips" with the dead, Old Iacob hadn't quite finished with the "ammunition" - but we still waited. We were still waiting.

I waited on the *calidor*. Sometimes I waited there for two

or three days at a time: since the Romanians liberated the town of Balta, over the Dniester, some of the people who'd been pulled in a short while before the beginning of the war started to return home. Father had been pulled in a long time before the war, but that didn't matter. Mother found out who had come back and which village they were from, and she went there to see if she could find anything out. Sometimes she came back crying, other times she was nearly rejoicing, the last journey she came back from, she was crying - no news or bad news.

But that was nothing. With her former colleagues from teacher training college and other women teachers, Mother had formed a "network" - that's what she called it; women teachers throughout the whole of Basarabia and Bukovina kept in contact: if one of them somehow found out that someone who'd been pulled in had since returned, she went to question him (as Mother did for the monograph), about where they'd been, with whom, what they'd heard about others who'd been there - and then she sent telegrams to the other women. If there was something interesting - but everything was interesting as far as Mother was concerned, that's why she was always on the move - to Cahul and to Hotin, to Cetatea Alba and to Soroca, she came home only for as long as it took to find out whether any telegrams had arrived in connection with... And of course, some had come, others hadn't - telegrams in connection with...

Old Iacob was more fortunate; he was always, always saying:

"If not today, then t'morrow!" - and also, "Don't worry, the Lord is mighty an' good..."

Late in the autumn, Mother stopped receiving telegrams, and stopped going - to Cernauti and to Ismail, to Balti and to Calarasi. Late in the autumn Mother started wearing black. That was it. There was no hope at all. Old Iacob carved a cross and dug a grave next to my little brother Peter's. All of us from the village went to the funeral.

Dodon, the priest who'd returned from refuge, and Grosu, the teacher, sang mournfully but beautifully. And that was it.

That was it, I was a little orphan - as Aunt Domnica said.

From then on, I could get up to any kind of mischief, any kind of devilment (as Old Iacob said) and people wouldn't get annoyed at all, they'd say :

"He's a littl' orphan, the poor mite..."

Oh, The Girls!

I'm sitting on the *calidor*. Sitting there - and that's all.
That's all because after Father's funeral the memories don't
flow any more. They leap. Like locusts. From here, from
who knows where. But no: not from who-knows-where but
from where-I-don't-expect-them, but they always come to
land down here, on the *calidor*.

The girls, for instance: let's take Tuza as an example. She
just appeared - I can't remember when she came to stay with
us - it was after my mother took my father's job as head of
the school, and she came to take over Mother's former
position. Was it autumn '41? Or the following year, when I
first entered school?

Anyway, a new schoolmistress came with a strange name:
Sarmisegetuza (I called her Tuza, I didn't manage to
pronounce her full name until much much later). She came
from miles and miles away, from a town with a beautiful
name: Alba Iulia, and from a province with a name that was
just as beautiful: Transylvania. (That's what Mother called it,
but Tuza called it something else, something horrible, the
Ardeal*...that was it, and it didn't seem right that a province
had to burn, just because she said so, even if she came from
there.)

Everything about the young lady was new: her clothes
and suitcases and satchel. Even the way she spoke, in a
drawl, and what she did when she was surprised: "Beggars!"
she'd say, and we used to laugh...

And something else new to us, was that Miss Tuza didn't
like it in our parts: she didn't like Basarabia, and she didn't

---

Ardeal - alternative name for Transylvania favoured by the inhabitants (especially
the ethnic Hungarians) of the region. Roughly means *burning hill*.

like the Orhei region - and she especially didn't like it here in Mana. She said there was too much mud here, and too much dust, and too much snow in winter ("I've only seen the like at the movies!" she said), and it was too icy ("My bowels will freeze up!" she said, but we pretended we hadn't heard, because not even the peasants said that where we lived). She was always complaining that there were no movies and that she couldn't go for a walk on the Corso - as she could at home in Alba Iulia, or in Sibiu, where she went to teacher training college.

Mother bit her tongue for as long as she could, until one day she said to her,

"My dear girl, if you don't like it, why on earth do you stay here? Ask for a different school in another region, Romania's a big country..."

"It's not any more, the Hungarians took the Ardeal from us and it's only small again," said Tuza.

"That's true, but in any case it's certainly big enough for the both of us. Ask for a school in a town like your town, Alba Iulia, then you can have both the movies and the Corso, as you call them..."

"Yes, but I didn't get good enough grades," said Tuza. "With the grades I got, they shoved me here. If I'd made the grades, I wouldn't have come to this wretched place..."

Mother got especially annoyed when the young lady used the word "wretched", even after she found out that in the Ardeal, where Tuza came from, when you said "wretched" you really meant "something insignificant" or "a trifle", and that in that Ardeal of theirs they call a wretched man "wiped out" - which made Mother smile, because in our parts "wiped out" means what it says, "perished" or "gone astray", but not by itself - like a man in a forest - but like when you have something and then you don't have it any more; or like money, you pay everything you've got and get nothing...

Miss Tuza was incessantly complaining that here - in this wretched place - she had no distractions and no "entourage"... Mother said she should have thought about that when she started teacher training and not now she'd finished; and that a teacher in the country was expected to organise the distractions and "entourage" as the country folk expect him to, since his mission is to do something for other people, not for himself.

Tuza didn't understand what Mother was telling her. She said, "But Madam, I'm a young lady, not so old like you that I don't feel the need to do things anymore ... You don't even try to keep yourself young, but walk around in black all the time ... and I'm from the Ardeal, Madam, and in our parts people are ci-vi-lised, not like here..."

Mother coughed and kept calm - Tuza was staying with us, and you were supposed to behave more ci-vi-lised with your hosts. She said:

"Well, I've never been to your parts, but I've heard about it. You were occupied by the Hungarians for nigh on a thousand years and after that by the Germans, but when you gained your independence in 1918, you were much more ci-vi-lised than the Moldavians and the Wallachians who'd been free for a long time. Mind you, we were under the Russians for a hundred years - but they made us go back three hundred..."

"I don't know why you all keep going on about these hundreds of years," Tuza said, "but I know what the Hungarians did to us, they broke us on the wheel, Madam, and they strung us up."

"The Russians might not have broken us on the wheel or strung us up, but they prohibited schools from using Romanian as the language of instruction - the Hungarians didn't do *that* to you..."

"What do you know about what the Hungarians did to us?!"

"Well, I know what they *didn't* do to you - but the Russians, what they did to us... They banned our schools, they didn't let us have cultural societies or libraries or printing presses that used the Romanian language. And we never had any Romanian representatives in Petersburg, like you had in Budapest..."

"What do I care about representatives and Budapest...I just know I don't like it here. And it's no fault of mine - I couldn't even find a rea-son-a-ble landlord in the whole village..."

"What do you need a landlord for when you're staying with us, like part of the family?" Mother asked. "Don't you like it here with us?"

"Of course I do! It's reasonable here, I'm not saying anything to the contrary..."

Later, I found out just what a reasonable landlord meant: firstly, wooden floorboards, not clay; secondly - as Mother was to say much later - reasonable means that you pay no rent, you pay for nothing at all, and you send three-quarters of your salary back to Alba Iulia; and you don't like the food that Mother makes, but you eat it and ask for more anyway; and you don't make your bed and you don't wash your underwear but put it in our basket for Mother to wash, just like that! as if you didn't even realise what you were doing.

"My dear girl," said Mother, "I'm sorry we have to discuss such things - but you know well enough that I haven't got a cart or a sleigh to use to gather firewood, and that I pay a man to chop it for me - it wouldn't be a bad idea if you contributed in some way toward the heating..."

"But *I* don't make the fire. What, do you want me to start making the fire?" - it was true, she didn't help to get the fire going.

"No, don't worry about that, I can get the fire going, that's not too difficult, I just meant that the wood is rather expensive... It takes up one whole salary, and with a small child, let's say that..."

"I didn't force you to have a child!" - that was true as well - "and the fireplace isn't in my room."

That was even more true: we had bought a large brick

heater which warmed up both rooms. We made the fire in the drawing room, where Mother and I slept, while Miss slept in the bedroom, and the fireplace wasn't in there.

Much later, Mother told my father:

"She didn't have good enough grades, so she said, and so they sent her to this wretched place - as a teacher, she was all pie-in-the-sky - but she was quick off the mark in other things, like an engine... I couldn't even call her a miser, a miser knows very well that he's a miser and he keeps a tight hold of his purse strings and, sometimes, if you corner him and he doesn't actually open his purse, he'll at least turn red, because he knows he's a miser. Whereas that girl, the capital of Dacia (Tuza's name)... In her own way, she was quite bright and cheerful: but as far as she was concerned, everything was owed to her and she didn't owe anybody anything. In other words, she stayed in our house a whole autumn and winter... I dropped a few hints, something towards the firewood at least - nothing. Well, in for a penny, in for a pound, she ate what we ate, slept in our house... And mind you, it wouldn't have done me any harm to sleep in my own bedroom, would it? But, listen to this, there was one time when I needed a notebook - I hadn't been able to go to Orhei to buy the school supplies - anyway, I needed a school writing book, I can't remember how much they cost - let's say ten *lei*. I knew she had some spare and so I asked her if I could have one. My mistake, I should have said I wanted to borrow one... In she comes with the notebook and says 'Thirty *lei*.'

"I didn't understand and said, 'Oh, you're selling it to me, are you? - but why thirty *lei*, when they're only ten *lei* at Orhei?'

"And then she said, 'Well go to Orhei and buy one for ten.'

"And the silly Basarabian woman I am said, 'But I can't go, there's a storm blowing.'

" 'Do without it then. For thirty *lei* you've got the

125

notebook. Look, if you want two, I'll let you have them for fifty.'

"I thought she was joking. She wasn't. And I couldn't say anything. I got out thirty *lei* and gave it to her. I didn't think she'd take it. She took it, all right. And it wouldn't have been so bad if she hadn't said anything, but she said, 'I'm alone here among strangers, nobody has helped me with anything, I've had to manage by myself and I don't own a paper mill, I bought them with my own money...'

"I still hoped she'd recover her senses, but nothing of the kind! I wasn't going to be the one to remind her that she wasn't alone among strangers and that even though she didn't have her Corso here and her 'entourage', she had her lodgings, she had her own room, in our house, she ate with us - and the only thing I ever asked of her was a contribution towards the wood. The notebook - to hell with the notebook! But let her tell me once more that in my house, which was just as much her house for six months, nobody helped her, that she had to manage by herself... I said to myself - best to go our separate ways..."

But until we did go our separate ways...I remember one time, about the underwear:

"My dear girl," Mother said, "if I had wanted somebody else to feed and wash for, I would have found myself a man!"

"If you can find two, the better-looking one's mine!" Tuza said. "But he's got to be rich, though, otherwise..."

Otherwise forget it, as she would say. Then a while later,

"My dear girl, at least wash your own panties - for heaven's sake!"

"What, with my own hands?" Tuza said, holding out her hands in astonishment.

"Why, what's wrong with your hands? Who washes them for you at home?"

"I do. But when I was at home, I was a pupil on holiday. I'm a schoolteacher now!"

"And because you're a schoolteacher, that means the

headmistress has to wash them for you?"

"I hadn't thought of that," said Tuza. "In that case, I'd better find another landlady - but rea-son-ab-le..."

But until she moved to another, rea-son-ab-le landlady...

I was fond of her. She wasn't very pretty, in fact when she was in the light you could see that she had rather spotty cheeks. And she walked like a man. And she was quite skinny. And she was a bit wall-eyed. But if you looked at her from the side you couldn't tell. I was fond of her from the side and when there wasn't much light.

When Mother was taking classes in the morning (with the second to fourth years - I was in Miss's class, the first year), Tuza stayed in bed until quite late. And she called me to her room to have a chat. Because I was only wearing a night-shirt and was barefoot, my feet were cold and I used to sit on them. And so Miss would say that if I was cold, I should come in. Into the warmth. I pretended I didn't really want to, then I got in.

We stayed like that for a while, without moving, side by side and flat on our backs. Then Miss would roll towards me and ask me something, anything. And she stroked me on the forehead and on the cheeks. And she asked me again if I wasn't cold, because she was cold. And she asked me to tell her how freezing people in Basarabia managed to warm up. And I told her how. And she told me to show her just how it was done - I would play the part of the man numbed with cold and she would be the young girl who thaws him out. I told her that for every numb man, you needed at least two girls, one to lie on either side of him; she said that for the time being there was only one girl - the other one would come later - but couldn't we try anyway just with one? And so we tried. I took off my night-shirt, she got undressed as well and we both pressed against each other. First of all, I pressed my back against her to thaw out my spine; then I thawed out my chest, then she said that she wanted to be the numb one and I could be the third girl, the one who lies on

127

top; then we changed places and she was on top, but I didn't like that as much because she pressed on me too hard and nearly crushed me.

Another time, she said that it would be good if I got inside her night-shirt; but I didn't really like that either because she tickled this side and that side, up here and down there - and I couldn't escape until she let me out herself.

One day, she asked me what it had been like with Tecla, and what the servant girl had done to me to make Mother throw her out. I told her, firstly, Tecla wasn't a servant, she was a girl helping us out; secondly, it wasn't proper for me to say anything, Tecla had told me so; and thirdly and connected to my firstly, that if she said Tecla was a servant, it wasn't proper for her, Miss Schoolteacher, to know about what servants get up to. But she said why shouldn't it be proper - all girls were made the same way. She told me to take a good look at her and then see if I could say that she wasn't made the same way as Tecla. I told her that I hadn't seen with my eyes, because there wasn't enough light over there on the old kitchen stove, but that I could try without any light under the blanket, if she wanted. And so I had a go. And I told her that she was nearly exactly the same. And she told me that if she was the same then we could do what I had done with Tecla, couldn't we?

We did, but it wasn't the same as it had been with Tecla. I said that if she wanted to - and she did - we could climb onto the stove so it would be exactly the same. We got onto the stove and did just about exactly the same - and, exactly, Mother caught us and told the young lady to pack her bags.

I felt sorry for her, but I was more sorry that I hadn't been able to show her the honey bear. I didn't have time. So sorry that one morning, when Mother was at school, I nipped out of the house and went to Severin's, Miss's new landlord. It was spring and the whole village was out in the fields - and Severin, the most hard-working of the men in Mana, would have got there first. I went into the yard, into the house and opened the door of Miss's room. But I closed it straight away and left: Miss didn't need me to show her the honey bear any more, Old Severin was showing her.

Come to think of it, I wasn't too sad: Tuza wasn't from our parts anyway. And she was always talking too much if I tried to show her anything. And always asking lots of questions, how you did this, what it had been like with another girl - around our way the girls didn't ask me questions all the time, they just showed me what they had to show and afterwards told me I'd better not tell anybody. A few of them used to say things, but they didn't use the ugly words Miss Tuza did.

Tecla - she used to say things - but how nice they were! And how gently she used to hold and caress me and how beautifully she used to show me this or that. Tecla came and went but Lina stayed, she was always around. And when I didn't have anyone else, I used to look for Lina. In fact, I didn't even have to look for her, I only had to go when she called me.

Her dad was a waggoner and her mother worked days here and there, which meant that most of the time Lina was alone at home. She had finished the four years of primary school a long time ago, so she must have been about twelve or thirteen. In the winter, when it was very cold, or even when it wasn't winter but was horrid outside, we used to hide ourselves in between bales of wool in a cold room at her house. In summer, we hid in the heaps of corn cobs in the yard, or in straw, or in haystacks - it depended.

Lina didn't talk very much, as a matter of fact her nickname was Dumbo, she only smiled and giggled, but her cheeks used to go so red sometimes, that it seemed like she was talking to them, or to her eyes. She had green eyes, green and gold, but the whites were a bit bloodshot; and her mouth was pinker than pink; and her little birdy was even pinker. Sometimes, when I was playing in the yard in front of our house, Lina would be busy in the alley, at our fence -

giggling. She didn't say a word, but when I saw her pink mouth I knew she was calling me to go and play with the little pink birdy. I sneaked out through the gardens - Mother didn't let me play with Lina, I don't know why and she didn't explain, she only said that that girl would end up in real trouble. I didn't understand and I wasn't really bothered about what Mother said - as long as she didn't catch me with her, because then she'd hit me. But as long as I sneaked out through the gardens and returned by the same route, I wouldn't get hit. Dumbo giggled all of the time, pinker than pink. Even when there wasn't any light where we were hiding, Lina was pink and blushing. And we played lovely games.

It was something else with Duda, but not for long, and now she doesn't even take any notice of me.

And something else again with Tecla. To say nothing of Balana...

I wonder what the experiences of the other boys my age were like in Mana? Even if they had them too, not one of them told me about it. Like me - they didn't breathe a word - besides, the girls, the big and the small, before, during and especially afterwards said to me, "You'd better not tell anyone!" - even Dumbo said that - those were the only words I ever heard from her little pink mouth. Perhaps I might have been an exception? Because I was the teacher's son? Or because I'd become a poor little orphan? Perhaps both, or neither. Were the Basarabian girls more "quick off the mark", as we say about those women who love to be loved? Or perhaps the morals in our parts were more...easy?

I've no idea - I don't think so though: a bride who wasn't a virgin brought shame not only on her family but on the whole village; and if a wife took a step out of line, the husband had to pay, sometimes with his life, while she had to try her fortune in some other village, miles away. I remember the "handkerchief game" at weddings, where a blood-stained handkerchief was waved about, proof that the bride had been a virgin. I heard all kinds of talk about a "seam", about the "blood of a homing pigeon", which I hadn't understood at the time although I knew that it was something to do with a girl's honour; but even that wasn't too clear because some girls had told me that their honour was their little birdy, which had to be honoured by your little birdy. That's what Tecla told me the first time, but others have told me that as well - the older ones, naturally.

Tecla was from around Tighina. And she was beautiful, like the Queen of Spades: jet-black hair and greener-than-green eyes. With gold in them. *She* had been staying with us for a while - Miss Tuza, that is - but she hadn't got around to calling me in to show her anything.

I didn't have anything to show her anyway, because I didn't know then what I'm going to tell you now.

We were in the kitchen one morning. I didn't really feel like eating anything. Mother had told Tecla to keep trying to make me eat, and to force me, if necessary. I heard her saying so, but I wasn't going to let myself be forced. Tecla was trying to force the food into my mouth and I told her that if she did it again I would bite her on the end. She looked at me with huge green eyes. And laughed.

"Really? Well then, if you bite my end, I'll bite your end!"

"You say that," I said, "but you don't say it out loud because it's not proper."

"I can say it out loud if I want to," said Tecla. "I started with two, that means I've still got one left, but you only had one, so how many have you got left?"

I thought about it and said, "Fair enough. In that case I'll bite your other end as well. Now what have you got left?"

"Fair enough," Tecla echoed, "Look, this is what we'll do; I'll eat your food and you can tell your mother that you've eaten it - shall we do that?"

"No! Only I can eat my food. I'll give my food to you, if you give something to me."

"Deal!" said Tecla. "Right then, I'll give this food to you, if you eat it. There, I've given you it, eat it!"

She thought I was a child and that she could trick me. I told her,

"I am an orphan and I know about lots of things. And if you want to know, I know what you look like everywhere - are you going to show me so I can prove that I know?"

"I'm an orphan as well and I know about lots of things. Look, this is what we'll do: you be a nice little orphan and eat this all up, and after that, this little orphan will give you something - but you'd better not tell anyone!"

Aha! I got up from the chair.

"Can I look up there?" I asked.

"If you eat up your food, I'll even let you look down there," Tecla said.

And so I wolfed down every morsel I'd refused until then. Tecla locked the kitchen door and told me we were going to get onto the stove. It's nice on the stove in winter. She took all her clothes off, and then took mine off as well.

When I saw it, I was a bit scared - I hadn't seen Duda's, and Lina's was pink and pretty. Tecla calmed me down, and said that that's how it was with orphans, that's how I would be very soon, because we orphans grow up more quickly than other people. Really? Yes. In fact, it was even prettier with some black around the red. I didn't have any, but very soon I would. Tecla told me that we orphans could do it like this, and like this, and like this, we could do whatever we liked best - as long as we didn't tell anybody else about it, who wasn't an orphan like us.

There was a storm blowing outside and it had become nearly dark beside the stove, but I could see everything we were doing. The darkness was warm and good and smelled a bit spicy when I went in - and it was so-so when she told me that we were licking the honey bear. And after the bear came the horse - we took turns as rider, I kept tight hold of her little reins when I was riding and just as tight when we fell over. Tecla might have had two eyes and two ears and two feet and two hands and two nipples, but she had lots of mouths. I asked her how many she had, and she said she had what she needed, and even more than she needed.

That was the timetable in the mornings. We waited until the noise from the school died down, and, after I'd eaten up my food like a good boy, and I was sure that Miss hadn't woken up, we locked the kitchen door and climbed up onto the stove, where Tecla had all kinds of mouths.

But one day, Mother came home to look for something and found the kitchen door locked. And so ... Tecla left, together with her green eyes and her pink mouths.

In her place came an older woman. I was always telling her that I didn't want to eat anything, but ... she said I could do what I liked for all she cared, waste not want not, so the saying goes. Which means ... nothing. As luck would have it, she went to her own village one Saturday and didn't come back. Good riddance! She was ugly. And stupid.

And then, of course, there was Balana. I didn't know what her real name was, but that's what Mother used to call her. Perhaps her surname was Balan? Or perhaps it was because she had golden blonde hair and cornflower blue eyes (*balan* means "flaxen").

She had deep blue eyes and she was always frightened: she would jump at the slightest sound and spit across her chest. And cross herself. She wore a lovely flowered skirt and little red ankle boots with high heels.

The first time I saw her in our kitchen, I noticed her little boots. About two days later I pretended I had things to do in the kitchen so I could have another look at them. The thing I liked best was when she came in from outside, where she'd been busy drawing water or bringing in the wood, and she took them off to put her slippers on. I sat there with my eyes glued to the boots. Perhaps that's why it took such a long time for me to remember that I wasn't eating.

"I'm not going to eat," I said. "And if I don't eat, I'll

133

die."

Balana got terribly frightened and spat across her chest. She tried coaxing me - I wasn't having any of that; she tried threatening me - none of that either. She took it from the beginning again:

"If you eat it up, I'll tell you a beautiful story."

"I don't like stories. I'm not going to eat - anything else?"

"If you eat it up, I'll sing you the most beautiful song you've ever heard."

"I don't want to hear a song. I just want to not eat a thing and to die. And if I die, Mother will beat you and throw you out!"

Balana crossed herself and spat across her chest. Then she started searching, desperately - she said she'd give me her pearls: I didn't need her pearls, I was a boy, wasn't I? Well, she'd give me her prayerbook, then. But mine was better anyway: the icons were in colour in my prayerbook.

"Well, what do you want, then? What on earth can I give you to make you eat?"

"The little red boots."

Balana made an Oh! sound that was half-frightened, half-rejoicing, and spat across her chest, then came to the point: how could she give me her boots? It was winter, it was cold outside, what could she put on when she went out for the water or the wood? And anyway, what would I want with her boots, they'd be too big for my feet in any case, wouldn't they?

"They're not for my feet. They're for my prick."

Balana didn't understand. I hadn't understood either, the first time with Tecla. So I explained to Balana. No use, she stuck to what she was saying: she couldn't give them to me. Anyway, somebody had given them to her. For something.

"What for, what something?" I asked. "Something like you lying down with him?"

Balana didn't spit across her chest this time; she gave a

134

long Oh! and burst into tears. I put my hand on her shoulder and said to her:

"If you lie with me as well, I'll give you them too."

She didn't understand that either: how could I possibly give her something which was hers anyway, on her feet - look at them! I explained:

"Look, this is what we'll do: you take them off and give them to me. If you don't lie with me, I won't give them back to you. If you do, then I'll give you a pair of nice little red ankle boots - and besides that, I'll eat as well and Mother won't beat you because you let me die and she won't throw you out."

Whatever Balana might have been thinking, she said:

"So that's the custom round here, is it? But if I lie with you, will you really give me the boots? 'Cause if you don't keep your word, God'll beat *you*!"

She took the boots off and held them out to me. Then she pulled them back only to offer them to me again:

"Now give 'em to me!" she implored.

"I said I'd give you them afterwards - that's what happened with *him*, didn't it? He gave you them afterwards. Or did he give you them first?"

"I'll have to think about it," said Balana. "Let me think, yes, he gave me 'em first. No! Come to think of it, he gave me 'em after... No, wait! He gave me 'em before. And afterwards..."

"In that case, I'll give you them first, as well," I said and held them out to her. "So first, I give these to yoooou..."

"No! Wait!" Balana said. "Wait 'til I've thought about it..."

And she thought and thought - for such a long time that she forgot what she was supposed to be thinking about. "I've remembered now!" she shouted. "He gave me 'em afterwards, 'cause I was crying."

"What were you crying for?" I asked her. "Had your mother been hitting you?"

135

"No, my mother hadn't been hitting me, I haven't got a mother. I haven't got a father either - but that's what... That's what you're supposed to do afterwards, you cry afterwards..."

"In that case, I'll give you the boots after you cry."

"Why do I have to cry?" Balana cried without meaning to. "The little boots are mine, they belong to me!" - and she snatched them back and pressed them to her chest, and stopped crying.

"Well, if that's how you're going to act, I'm not going to eat. And I'll die! And Mother..."

"No, don't die! Come on, eat it up..."

"I'll only eat *after* I've given you the ankle boots."

"Oh, re-a-ll-y? Well, alright then: come on, give 'em to me."

"Are you stupid, Balana? Didn't I tell you that I'd give them to you after we lay down together? After you had a good cry?"

"And just where are we going to lie down? There's no hay here."

"But there's the stove," I said.

I climbed up, then she climbed up. I told her to take her clothes off. She said, Heavens above! she'd never got undressed in front of anybody before. I told her what I'd heard, that there was a first time for everything. And that, if she really wanted the little red boots, if she really didn't want me to die... Crying, she took her clothes off. When she started really sobbing, she suddenly broke into a laugh:

"But you're only a child, what are you going to use to lie with me?"

I showed her what I was going to use. She spat across her bare breasts and made the sign of the cross. And she cried and laughed.

And so we had a nice time. And we kept playing the laugh-cry-and-give-me-the-boots game. When Mother was at school in the mornings, I sat down at the table and said that

I wasn't going to eat a thing. She asked me why not. I told her that because if I didn't, I would die. She started crying and asked me what she could possibly give me to prevent me from dying. And I said:

"Don't cry, I'll give you the little boots."

And, so that I had something to give her, she gave them to me first. And after the stove, I gave them to her. And it was nice. In fact, it was so nice, that one day I even forgot that I wasn't going to eat first. She cried, took her boots off, gave them to me and asked me to give them back to her afterwards.

Balana stayed with us for a long time. Summer came, and she walked about barefoot inside the kitchen and outside, but, when the time came, she got the little red ankle boots out of the trunk, which is what she called the suitcase, and gave them to me - so I could give them to her.

And I always gave them to her. God only knows how Mother never caught us.

After Balana left to get married in another village, we didn't employ another girl to help out. And so I went back to Lina. Who, I found, had changed: she had black around the pink now.

But even when I was with Lina, I was thinking about my little Balana. And about my little Tecla. What good and beautiful girls they were!

Fishes and Hats

Last night the dam burst at the monastery at Curchi. I knew about it before I saw it. Old Iacob knocked at our window:

"Missus! Missus! Don't wake up th' littl' fellow, but th' dam's burst at Curchi. Don't be afraid, but I thought you sh'd know..."

Well, of course the little fellow woke up, got dressed with the speed of a little soldier and tried to go outside.

"Get to bed at once, it's turned midnight!" Mother said, getting ready herself. "It's raining outside, there's nothing for you to see."

"I want to see what it sounds like," I said.

"All right, but don't you leave the *calidor*."

I sat there, shivering. You couldn't really see what it sounded like. Apart from the rain. If it hadn't been raining you could have heard the roar of the high flood from the burst dam, like you could two years ago. But I could see the roaring because I could hear the lanterns jingling. I couldn't tell whether the street lanterns were moving nearby in the courtyards and in the back lane, or whether the sound was coming from further away, at Horse Common; or perhaps beyond the main road, at Cattle Meadow. That's what the lanterns did, when it rained.

All around, I could hear sleepy voices just beginning to wake up:

"Com' on, man, it's burst!"

"Get yer horse ready, I'll get mine an' we'll go fishin' wi' the cart!"

"No, I'm goin' horseback - you go horseback too!"

"An' where 're you goin' to put 'em then, on horseback? 'Cross the pummel? Under the saddle? Or in yer pocket?"

"I'll find a place, so they're not untidy..."

"Hey, take some spades wi' you, we'll plug it up here, at our own dam!"

"You plug it up then, an' we'll do the fishin' and go halves."

"That's wha' we did two years back, we worked our backsides off diggin' - an' you went fishin', not wi' us blockin' the dam - an' then you split 'em in two, but wi' your father-in-law. How about swoppin' places?"

Hearty laughs, rounded off in the rain.

So, our dam had burst as well. It had burst earlier, when the bombs dropped and the front was here and all summer long the cattle grazed at the bottom of it. But it had been built up again, and I helped, either knocking in the poles, or carrying the clay... All the children helped, but look, it had burst again. It hadn't held when the high flood came down from the burst dam at Curchi - but from which one? The monks had five dams, four of them next to one another, and a fifth which was separate, on another river.

Splodge-splodge, splodge-splodge, bare feet in the mud of the back lane; the clattering of empty pails, the clinking of one iron tool knocking against another. And then, the commanding voice of Old Iacob as mayor:

"Everybody's to come wi' me, to Curchi! To plug up th' dam! A fine for anybody what doesn't come!"

"All right, Old Iacob: you go on ahead 'n' we'll catch you up... Wha' d' you say, man? Ha-ha-haaa!"

"You're a pack o' thieves, that's what y'are! You're only good for thievin'!"

"What d'you mean: thievin', Old Iacob? They swam away from th' monks, down t' where th' light shines here."

"Th' light'll shine on you, when they call you in for trial!"

"Why sh'd they? The fishes belong to the man 'at catches 'em, they're not branded, like the cattle. Wha' d'you think? Th' monks 'ave been takin' special care of 'em? Doin' 'em over with a currycomb? Waterin' 'em - he-ha-haaa! They come down by His grace an' belong to 'im what catches 'em - but better not tell the neighbours, neighbours are like strangers..."

Old Iacob started bellowing, trying to establish order in the "commune", but gave up. I heard him coming back into his yard. And then, in a different voice:

"Hey, woman! Domnica, where are you? Come an' pull these boots off my feet! An' give me a basket, better make it two, one'll break. An' give me a lantern."

"But you're the mayor, Iacob!" Aunt Domnica protested from the porch, strapping up her sandals to go out to pull his boots off. "What are you goin' to tell 'em t'morrow, when they come t' look for you, t' get yer report? What're you goin' to say? You've got your duties as mayor!"

"T'morrow's t'morrow, now it's th' dead o' night, an' I'm goin' to get myself a bit o' fried carp; an' some pike grilled in th' embers; an' some tench wi' a sip o' gin; an' if God above's good enough, I'll land a bit o' eel, one o' the big ones... An' give me a net as well - for th' crayfish... T'morrow I'll say, what was I supposed t' do, all alone, in th' darkness an' in the rain? It was so dark you couldn't even see th' back of yer neck - ha ha haa!"

"Ha ha haa!" Aunt Domnica echoed, "These men from Mana! Brain's only big enough for pinchin' and pilferin'. At home, at Chistruieni, all of us old and young would've gone out to plug up the dam! Not out thievin'!"

"At 'ome, at 'ome, you an' your Chistruieni! At 'ome, you still plug up the dam with your coats, 'cause it's your dam, it belongs to th' commune - but this one? D' you expect th' monks to plug it up with their cassocks?"

"But this one's yours - I mean ours. And if this one of ours bursts, who's goin' to build it up?"

"This one of ours!" Old Iacob mimicked her, speaking like the people from around her way, at Chistruieni. "What should we plug this one of ours up for now? We'll plug it up when we've caught all th' fish. He knows, God knows how to

140

arrange things - if those scoundrels in Mana hadn't forced it to break...we're nearly drowned by it when we go out after th' fish... An' anyway, if it was our dam, I'd 've pressed my whole chest against it to plug it up!"

"You'd have put yer... I knoooow you, Iacob, I know what you'd've stuck in where it was burst - forgive the language: yer belly..." and the old woman started laughing.

"An' if you want t' know, I can tell you that th' monks plugged theirs up as well! But all for nothin': only for it to drain out again into where the sun shines on us - it'd be a deadly sin for us not to feast ourselves on what th' Lord God's sent us..."

That was Old Iacob: mayor he might have been, but he was still a Manian. Aunt Domnica was just a "foreigner", she came from another place - that was why she was working all the time, as if she wanted to get to heaven in a hurry... That was why she was always grumbling at her husband, as Manian as they came...

I was sitting on the *calidor*, trembling. Mother came out several times as well: to give me something to put on, or to bring me something to eat. But I wasn't trembling because of the cold, nor because I was hungry. This time, if I'd wanted to - and I did want to - I could have sneaked out of the house. All alone, finding my way by following the lights, until I got down there, where the monks' dam had reached us. If I'd asked Old Iacob really nicely, perhaps he would have taken me with him: I could have held the light, or the basket full of fish... Old Iacob didn't have a cart, otherwise we'd have taken the cart when we went after the fish, there were so many when the dams burst. And even when they didn't burst, it was the same.

You couldn't go bathing around our way, there were so many fish. Where we lived, if a cow wanted a drink, if it went to the stream it swallowed fish as well - that's what they said, it wasn't quite like that, but there was some truth in it: around our way, only Old Iacob played about with a fishing rod - Father had given it to him and he was ashamed not to take it with him, but I knew that he didn't catch the fish with the rod, he used a trawling net: you threw it in the water, walked along with it for about ten steps and you took it out: full! It wasn't really completely full, but a quarter of it was. And that was when the dams were sound, but when they burst, because of the rain... You couldn't put your foot in the water without stepping on something.

I would have gone with Old Iacob, but I stayed on the *calidor*. Not because I'd have been afraid of the dark down there where the fishes were, or because of the pouring rain, but because I didn't like it. To tell the truth, though, it was the pouring rain that I didn't like - up above it was raining, down below it was running in torrents... Better to stay put.

Fish weren't for me, anyway. Because I was a Sir. I would have given up being a Sir, but that's not how Sir wanted it.

And so I sat on my *calidor*. When you sat there you could be absolutely anywhere you wanted to be, and you were always safe.

From what I'd heard so far, and from what I was to hear the next day and the day after, I knew. No longer a child, I knew what the prob-lem was - both for a Sir and for a Manian who'd gone fishing with a sack or with a little cart:

You'd caught a fish, a big fish, a monster as big as an ox - or as big as a calf, or a piglet, in any case, about as big as you were; you'd fought with it and wrestled with it for a whole hot summer's day and into the evening, in water up to your waist, or up to your knees; you'd lost your lantern and your reed basket. Should you put it into the bucket? It wouldn't fit in. Should you go back home with just him, only one fish no matter how big he was? Wasn't it a shame to leave the rest for others to catch or even worse, for nobody to catch? And so, where could you put the fish you'd caught after you'd got a good hold of it by the gills and given it a good whack on the back of its head with the mallet to send it off to sleep? Where could you put it, if you didn't put it in the sack? You'd lost the sack in the struggle, but a sack was easy to find, even in the dark: you looked for it with your feet, like a blind man. And, after you'd found it, what did you do? You put the fish inside it and flung the sack over your shoulder... Your shoulder?

"An' what's t' be done?" - that's what I heard and was to hear again.

"It's rainin' from above. An' a man in th' rain without a sack on 'is head's like a pan without a lid, a house with no roof, it rains straight down into 'is throat. But on th' other hand, th' fish - where d'you put it? Solve the prob-lem, Ion!"

That's what I heard and was to hear again.

"But what're you bothered about getting caught in the rain for?" Mother laughed when she heard the dreadful predicament related by Maxim or Oxinte or by Simion Cristea, two or three days after the dams burst. "You were dripping wet with the rain when you got there - a sack's a sack not an oilcloth; you rolled about in the water - you yourself said that you were wrestling with the fish - and so what if you got caught in the rain again? You should've been pleased to get the mud and all the rest washed off you!"

"Yes, well, Missus, you can tell that you're a lady an' that you've forgotten, if you ever knew in th' first place, that we peasants 've got prob-lems of our own..."

"I might be a lady," Mother said, "but my parents were peasants and I was a peasant - and still am for that matter, I'm still even living in the country..."

"I'm not sayin' any diff'rent, but your parents are peasants in th' hills, they haven't got a prob-lem wi' th' water, like us here."

"Problem! What problem - about putting a sack on your head? Do you really think that the Manian was the first man to put a sack on his head? And do you think you're the only person to put a sack over your head when it rains?"

"F'rgive me for sayin', Missus, but I've never seen you with a sack on yer head, only with 'n umbrella - but th' rain isn't th' problem, th' problem's somethin' else... An' I hope you don't think it disrespec'ful, but have you seen how people round here take a bath?"

"Yes I have. And so what? I have a bath as well."

"Well, we're not speakin' of women. But of people..."

"I see: women aren't people... Do you mean to say the men take a bath in their bare skin? Just how they like it!"

"It's not a matter o' likin' it, it's somethin' else. Like th' problem o' th' sack on yer head in th' rain - it still doesn't protect you, but it's a matter o'..."

"Don't get flustered. What's all this about taking a bath?"

"Well, then: a man, round here, when he wants t' take a bath, 'e takes all 'is clothes off - we don't walk about in our underpants, like th' boyars, we takes a bath just how our mothers made us, an' there's nothin' shameful in it, even if a man puts 'is hand over a little bit o' 'is front, for appearance' sake, that he's got somethin' t' hide. Or he might not hide it - naked as a babe - but you'll never get 'im t' take 'is hat off, unless you chop 'is head off an' take th' lot!"

"I know that," Mother said. "You see that in other parts as well, but they don't mumble on about it - but I don't see what the big problem is."

"Well, this's it: there'd be no better use for a hat, but y'see - forgive th' language - it's not this 'ere head that's th' shameful one, when a man's naked in 'is shame! A hat's a hat! A man without a hat on's more naked than nakedness itself. It's like th' sack. Without a sack on in th' rain, you're not a man..."

The Manian who was trying, in his own fumbling way, to explain the theory behind the sack and the hat, believed that the prob-lem existed only around there, in Mana - or at most in the neighbouring villages. Some years later, Father was to "discover" the same problem, in Transylvania - in another context:

"I thought that the most difficult thing, in the country,

was to persuade the girls and the women to ... show their legs
- for sports, I mean. If you explained it to them once or
twice, it was all right. Once one of them got undressed...
But you could forget about the schoolboys. You might've
been able to get them to accept the shorts, but the hat was a
completely different story: 'But look, Vasile, if you were in
the army, would you do sports in your vest and pants
and...with your helmet on your head?' I asked one of the
young mules. 'Yes, but th' army's th' army, an' I'm in my own
village here - without my hat on, I'm not a man!' I tried to
win them with the example of the girls, more shameful -
wouldn't everyone laugh if they came out onto the field with
their head-dresses on? 'A woman's a woman, shameless'...
And so the young lads - sorry, the bashful young boys -
played football, volleyball, handball, did the high jump,
threw the javelin...but with only one hand. With the other,
they kept tight hold of their hats on their heads. And so
things went, until the district championship - we had quite a
good football team... 'And what's up with your lot,
Comrade?' I was asked by the regional comrade who'd come
down to the district to shake our hands. I answered, 'You'll
see, they're just beginners...' 'What d'you mean, they're
beginners, they're perpetuators of inveterate enmity! I mean,
they want to make it obvious on the field, where the classes
are suppos'd to be brothers t'gether, that they're not too
well-disposed to being members of the collective - I'll hand
them over to the Militia (military police)!'

" 'What are you talking about, Comrade?' I asked him.
'About the hat!' I thought I wasn't on very safe ground
talking about ... the principles of the class struggle, so I
asked, 'But what has the hat got to do with ... the socialist
transformation of agriculture?' 'Plenty! If it hadn't, they
wouldn't come out here, in front of me, in front of a huge
crowd of spectators, with their *kulak* sabotage! It's provoca-
tion! I'm calling the Militia!' 'Don't worry, I'll sort it out,' I
said. And here the comedy ended and something else

145

began... I went to our players and told them that the blockhead who'd come down from regional headquarters was presenting us with a po-li-ti-cal problem: 'It has to be one or the other: either we present ourselves on the field without hats on - and may the best team win; or we accept defeat by default - but that won't be the end of it; he'll start an inquiry - we had wanted to present ourselves here, on a sports field belonging to the district, wearing...the sign of an individual peasant who doesn't want to be a member of...' They looked at each other and then all looked at me. One of them took his hat off and threw it down to the ground.

" 'Fuck th' district comrades an' th' regional comrades, th' cunts, they've taken our cornfields, an' cattle an' milk for their quotas; an' they've taken our land, an' ploughs, an' harrows for their collectives, an' now they want t' take my hat from me as well? No! I fer one am *not* givin' 'em my hat; and I shit on their football!' Others appeared more conciliatory - the fear had already started to work on them; while others said why shouldn't they play, what had they been working for all this time anyway? They started to take them off - you know how they do when they don't really want to; they roll their head to one side, tip their head over, keeping the hat directly in line with their hand... However, one of them said, 'An' you, Teacher-Sir, what d' you say? You're our teacher, what d' you teach us now? Should we do it? Or not do it, or what?' "

Father paused for a little while. And started to laugh, but only a little one and quietly like he did each time he related something from which he hadn't escaped quite unblemished:

"I started to shout at them: 'What can I say? What do you expect me to say, wasn't I the one who knocked at your doors to get you to hand your quotas over? Wasn't I the one who battered your doors and your brains to get you to join the collective?' 'But what 're you bawlin' at us for?' one of them said cantankerously, 'as if we were th' ones knockin' at *your* door, t' make *you* join the collective farm!' I said,

146

'That's just why I'm bawling - what kind of teacher am I, when I've made you do things that shouldn't be done, things in which I didn't believe?' 'What did you do 'em for then, if you didn't believe in 'em?' the devil said. 'Leave it, Rusalin', another one intervened, 'what, don't you know how times are now? An' if we're talkin' about door-knockin', the Headmaster knocked at yer door, him, yer uncle, and yer cousin Niculae - the big nob at the carpet factory...' 'Yes, but my uncle - *he* was ordered to, orders aren't discussed, he was headmaster in a school... An' as for cousin Niculae, they made 'im choose: either with 'em, the Communists, an' all that went with 'em, or back to prison, with them from the Iron Guard...' "

"Ah, I know who you're talking about now," Mother said.

" 'But look, you can talk about these things another time,' I intervened, 'this is the question: what are you going to do about the hats?' 'What can we do, when times 're like these? We'll put 'em on the grass, an' play...' They played and it so happened that they won and the boor from the regional headquarters didn't show up again... On the way home to the village - a jolly time; but something was gnawing at them.

" 'Teacher-Sir', said Rusalin, 'let's say you're like us, from th' village, an' wears a hat. Let's say, him from th' region tells you not t' wear yer hat any more, 'cause it's a sign of bein' a *kulak* - what w'd you do?' I tried to get out of it, and said that I'd never worn that kind of hat and so it wouldn't have any value for me... Rusalin insisted: well, couldn't I pretend I was one of them, from the village, and that the hat was of particular value to me...? ' Well then', I said, 'I think I'd have said what Gheorghe did: shit on their football, I for one am not givin' 'em my hat! - that's what I would have said!' 'Is that really what y'd 've said? But you told us t' play without our hats!' "

"But you didn't force them to play, you only told them what would happen if they didn't agree to part with their hats," Mother tried.

"That's all dead and buried now. Even when I knocked at their doors, I didn't force them, I only told them what would happen to them if... I said to them: 'Why? - out of fear. Out of fear for my own hide! For the same reason that *you* did your military service with the MAI (special police service) guarding the prisoners digging the canals!' 'Yeah, but the army's the army, orders 're carried out, not discussed!' 'If we're talking about orders being carried out, just you think about this, then: while I was knocking on your doors for your quotas and to get you to join the collective, I was bearing a heavy cross on my back - your uncle, the school headmaster and myself only just managed to carry out our orders... - but look what you got for yourself...special leave of absence, financial bonuses and the rank of corporal when you were transferred to the reserves...' 'Yeah, but in th' army, an order...' he started. 'Sure, an order - you carried out an order when you shot a prisoner - that's why you got your leave of absence, your rank, your thousand *lei* bonus - and don't try to deny it, your mother boasted about the heroic feats of her young son to me as well...' "

"What a good lad Baciu's Rusalin was," Mother said. "He saved his family from being classed as *kulaks* - they weren't, but neither were others who were classed as *kulaks* anyway - in with the *kulaks* not with the collective farmers - the ones who didn't have a son who could shoot at any other poor "*kulak*" in the canals... He was taken on again, still with them - the MAI - now he's guarding the prisoners as a salaried civil servant, at Gherla I think..."

"That's mankind for you," Father said. "But I'm not pricked by his conscience. I'm pricked by my own as a teacher, what's left of it. What we've ended up doing... And when you think that at one time we even used to call ourselves apostles... And what are we now? Salaried civil servants...what we've ended up as..."

"We've ended up being what they've made us be," sighed

148

Mother.

I wanted to ask Mother and Father: what would have happened if they'd refused to carry out their orders - knocking on the doors? What good would it have been? He said, without my asking him, under other circumstances:

"Perhaps nothing would have happened to us - but we weren't to know." Father was exaggerating: if you got five years for nothing - what would you have got for refusing?

He continued, "I don't know anyone - I personally don't - who might have refused to carry out their orders...among the village teachers, that is, who'd ended up being considered as 'everybody's grandmother '... The campaign for literacy which was delegated to them (but then, who else could have carried it off?), the cultural activities - the same again for them, sports activities - likewise. And since they were involved in all kinds of censuses - of people, of personal property and real estate, of animals, poultry, beehives - why shouldn't they be involved in 'enlightenment' as well? Even that was a campaign: at first to explain the quotas as a 'patriotic duty'; then to establish agricultural associations - to found 'a kind of co-operative, like Mihalache did'; and later to 'belong to' or 'enrol in' the co-operative farm... And I knew the rules of the 'enlightenment' game: perfect complicity. The enlighteners begged forgiveness for knocking on people's doors about such matters, the enlightened begged even more forgiveness from the enlighteners that *they*, the unenlightened, would remain unenlightened. *They* believed, and so did the others, the village teachers, that the Americans would come and change all wrongs into rights..."

But all this was to happen in the future, an unimaginable future - even as far as the Basarabians were concerned, who'd already had a taste of it - or were still having a taste of it, like Father, wherever he was, if he still was...

I was sitting on the *calidor* of the house in Mana and I was shaking. The same went for both the fish and the parachutes: my somewhat privileged position (as son of Teacher-Sir) excluded me completely from the category of...beneficiary. The reason, whose name I was to find out much later: *class struggle*, didn't have to be invented, it existed.

For example, if I were to get down from the *calidor* and pick up a lantern from somewhere and a reed basket - and even a sack to put over my head, so it wouldn't rain straight down into my throat - and were to go off quite alone across the common and all by myself, get through the mud and the water from the burst dam; and if I were to catch a little carp no bigger than my little finger - I wouldn't be able to get back home with it, so Mother could grill it for me, so I could eat fish that I had caught with my own hands. If we forget for the moment that Mother would fling me out of the house, fish and all, saying that she wasn't going to have her pans stinking of it, I wouldn't be able to offer her the chance of telling me off. And why? Because the Manians wouldn't have let me. They wouldn't have asked me, they'd have told me:

"Give that (or them) to me!"

Even before I could remember walking, I could remember being at the stream, with the children. Bathing in the water, splashing water at each other, jumping over the roots of a willow tree and making circles in the water with skimming stones. Because the oldest ones felt around under the roots and stones with their hands - even buried their hands under - and pulled out fish, I tried to do the same. As it turned out, I didn't catch anything and so I gave up, for a time.

Until about a few weeks ago; when I was paddling, I stepped on something, so I felt around and caught it - a fish. Not as big as a piglet, but it was certainly as big as the palm of my hand. I let it go - what was I supposed to do with it? Afterwards, however, I was eaten away with shame: what would my friends say if they found out that I had caught a fish, and had thrown it back into the water? I didn't know whether "that" was the done thing or not, but I hadn't seen anybody doing it. And so I set about looking. Looking for him, thinking that I'd catch the same one. And I started catching them, I even caught a little bream. I did what the other children did: I dug out a little lake at the edge of the water and put the fishes in there.

Then, from the opposite side of the stream, a boy said,

"You can give those to me."

"Why should I give them to you?" I said, surprised - the boy was about three years older than I was, but I wasn't frightened of him, I could thrash him whenever I wanted to, and with only one hand.

"Did you catch them?"

"No I didn't, but the fish aren't yours..."

What had got into him? He hadn't suddenly become stronger than the day before yesterday; he was alone, as well. And he was speaking to me like a grown-up.

"You reckon the village stream belongs to your father!" I said.

And he said, in the same grown-up way,

"We're agreed: those fish are mine. You can give them to me when we go back to the village."

He went further upstream and started talking to the other children. I told myself that they were getting ready to beat me up and take the fish from me by force; and then I said to myself: just let them try! I wasn't afraid of any of the children in the village. Not even of the older boys. I might have been smaller than some of them, I might have been a little orphan with no father at home to go and cry to, but I wasn't afraid: I knew how to defend myself - or rather, how to be the first one to attack...

I kept on searching under the roots and stones - and put the fish I caught into the little lake. The children didn't look as though they were thinking about coming to get me; but they weren't speaking to me either, even though I was

151

moving right beside them sometimes, right under their noses.

A man came along to water his cattle. I knew him, I'd taken milk from him before. The children, led by the little brat who said I had to give him the fish, went over to him and said something to him, pointing at me all the time. I knew what they'd said to the man: that they had caught the fish and that I had stolen them - and how was I going to prove that I had caught them? And so, when I saw that the man, surrounded by all the children, was walking over to me, I took the fish out of their little lake and flung them back into the water - off with the lot of them!

"A pity," the man said, taking his hat off and bowing to me like a grown-up.

"Pity or not, I caught them and I can do what I like with them!" I said. "Rather than have other people take them from me..."

"Well they wouldn't be takin' 'em from you, like they'd be takin' somethin' of yours. They'd be takin' th' fish. Anyway, better if you didn't catch any more, it'd be a shame t' spoil th' holiness o' th' fish..." - and he looked up into the valley, sorrowfully. "Perhaps you didn't know up 'til now; but round 'ere th' boyars and th' Jews only eat fish they pay for."

I was sitting on the *calidor* in the darkness and could hear the voices of the people on the common, where the flood was. And I was thinking about fish.

What was the point? I wasn't allowed to, unless I bought them - have you ever known Mother to buy fish! Hey, but if Father had been at home; if Father had been... he would have bought basketfuls and cartloads - and I'd have been able to eat fish as well, we could have sat down, us men together...

I hadn't really understood much of what that man said, he spoke like all grown-ups: using lots of long words so he wouldn't fall asleep... However, on the way back home, I remembered Old Iacob's "farthing":

152

The old man was always going fishing, with the fishing rod he'd received from Father over his shoulder (but only for appearance's sake, he had neither the confidence in nor the patience for the rod), but he never ever took me along with him. He said I was too small, that I'd frighten the fish, that we'd have to get up too early in the morning - and that I needed my sleep to grow. I would have been happy just to help him make the bait - he didn't need that either, but then did Old Iacob ever do only what he needed to anyway? I helped him, I mean I sat next to him the night before while he was getting it ready.

He called it the "shoots and toots",and even now it's not easy for me to accept that shoots or toots can mean anything other than ... bait: *mamaliga* dough which he kneaded in his hands for a long time, breathed over it, even spat on it - and then kneaded it again. Come to think of it, if fishing held any secret for me at all, that secret was the secret of ... the shoots and toots; I never knew if Old Iacob put anything else into the *mamaliga* (apart from spit), but I knew that fishing with a rod was something that I'd do as well - when I grew up (although that wasn't certain at all).

The real secret was this: Old Iacob got ready the night before, and the next morning when I woke up and went out onto the *calidor* to say good morning to him, the faint smell of cooked fish came wafting across from his house. He'd already returned home (after who knows how many, and how difficult, trials and tribulations).

And so all that was left for me to do was to welcome him back, to go back into the house, wash myself as quickly as possible, pick up my spoon and to join in - in the fish dish, just we two men (not even Aunt Domnica, who cooked it, would let any of it touch her lips...). And Old Iacob welcomed me:

"He-hey, my littl' friend, welcome, sit down, sit down," and he pointed to the little three-legged stool which was kept especially for me. "An' firstly then, an' firstly, Aunt

Domnica's goin' t' give us some carp borsch nice an' sharp, with lovage and toots (this time the toots were what they really were: 'wild' tomatoes, the size of cherries, which had no pips inside them and were much tastier than tomatoes with pips)... And with mama-mamaliga so good, yum-yum, you'll lick your fingers dry as wood... And both of us men'll fill our hats with two bowls full an' then tractor through another two! An' firstly an' secondly, some fish an' onions like only th' old girl knows how t' make, you don't taste it when you make it, that's th' secret. An' if we've got any room left, then firstly an' thirdly, some bream in cream, there you go, with garlic a dream..."

And Old Iacob recited his poetry - poetry because Aunt Domnica didn't quite give us what he said.

But one day, when we'd sat down at the low, round table, he asked me, as he usually did at the end of his little poem:

"Have you brought th' farthin'?"

The farthing! I'd forgotten it this time. I told him I'd go and get it after I'd eaten; for the very first time my own Old Iacob wouldn't let me do what I wanted to. He sent me, there and then, to fetch the farthing.

It was a little game of ours: at the very beginning, he'd given me an old coin, I didn't know how much money it was worth, but it didn't circulate any more. When it was a fish day - that was what the game was all about - after he'd finished his little poem, he asked me if I'd brought the farthing. I said I had. I gave it to him and after we'd finished eating, Old Iacob would give it back to me.

I went back home and returned with the farthing. But I stayed in the doorway.

"Old Iacob, I'm not a Jew, am I?"

"Where d'you come up wi' that? You're a Christian, my laddie!"

"Old Iacob, I'm not a boyar, am I?"

"Well, not really, not so far as I know!"

"Well if I'm not a Jew, and not a boyar, why do you

always ask me to give you the farthing?"

"Why ... because we're takin' parts, that's all ..."

"Why are we taking parts, if I'm not one or the other? Why do you make me pay, even in our game?"

Old Iacob couldn't think of what to say - he, Old Iacob, who had answers for everything! Aunt Domnica started grumbling at him again - hadn't she told him? But once a Manian always a Manian - tactless, what more was there to say?

I forgot all about the game with the fish. Mostly because he didn't invite me to eat with him again when he had some.

Sitting on the *calidor* I knew why not: I wasn't a boyar but I was a Sir. A tiny boyar, that is - that was why.

Parachutes

I was lying on the *calidor* of our house in Mana. I was lying spread out on a chaise longue and wrapped in blankets from the waist down. The autumn sun was setting to my left, low in the sky behind the forest. From here, from the *calidor* at sunset, could be seen more and more rose corollas floating and falling above the forest: parachutes.

We had got used to them. The sight and sound of their airplanes didn't stay with me, but time and time again I saw the parachutes coming down, like roses in the reddish light of dusk, towards the rust-coloured forest, as slowly as dandelion clocks in the still air.

"The parachutes! Let's go to the parachutes!"

The folk from Mana went after the parachutes as they went to the church fête; or after the fish when the dams burst. The young men, the biggest boys, the more tomboyish girls - as soon as they saw them they passed the word and went off after them as fast as they could - most of them went on foot, but some went on horseback or in carts, others went armed with poles, grappling irons, even with the iron hooks and claws that men use to climb up telegraph poles. The children weren't allowed to go. Children stayed at home. And waited. Sometimes they fell asleep wondering what their relatives who'd gone after the parachutes would bring them: the ropes and ties to play horses with? Perhaps even the parachute, out of which their mothers would make them nice shirts, the colour of butter - quite rough though, but didn't they call it rough-silk? Or perhaps they'd bring both?

I was lying on the *calidor* wrapped up in blankets. There weren't any men in my family, not even a tomboy sister to bring me back a little something from the forest; so to my great sorrow I wasn't going to be able to wear a butter-silk shirt. As usual, Mother would buy me a metre or two of the rigging from someone else, so I could play horses as well. Oh, I really wished I could be like the rest of them: walking about proudly with their shoulders back - showing off their parachute shirts - but where would I get one? Who was going to bring Mother silk - presuming she'd even accept it? There was no man in our house: Mother was a widow, I was an orphan: the Russians had pulled Father in about three years ago, I'd even forgotten what Father smelled like. True though, since spring I'd known that I wasn't completely an orphan and that Father was still living. In a camp. Mother said that it might be a camp, but all camps weren't the same: it was much better in the Soviet camps here in Romania than it was in a Soviet camp in Russia. When I asked her why it was better, she said that at least people came out of the Soviet camps in Romania - but I didn't understand: Father had come out of a Soviet camp in Russia, which was at the back of beyond, and had ended up here in Romania - but how come he hadn't left this one - if it was supposed to be better? Mother said it would be today-or-tomorrow and that the worst part was over - but I didn't really believe that. I was still a little orphan - because, well, Father wasn't at home and so he couldn't go racing into the forest at sunset, for the parachutes.

We had got used to the parachutists. At first we were afraid, the gendarme said they'd kill us - after they'd robbed us - but Old Iacob, who knew everything, told us how things stood:

" 'Course not! They're comin' with one idea in mind: to hand 'emselves over: *Predaite!* That's what they say in Russian..." And the old man put his hands right up into the air to show us how the parachutists gave themselves up.

And so, from then on, the villagers who earlier had only picked up what they found in the bushes or in the trees or under piles of dried leaves - after the parachutes had dropped, that is - now ran after "the shirts" as fast as they could, as soon as they saw them floating down. And they went hunting... In fact Morcov made himself a little nest in the cornel tree in the forest and waited there to pick the shirts out of the sky, and even boasted that two of them (one of which was a girl-shirt) fell right into his arms... The villagers helped anybody who had got caught up in the branches, or was hanging from the trees, to get down without breaking any bones. Then they undid their shirts, spread them out, cut them up and hid them...

"But what do they do with the people inside?" I asked Old Iacob, who knew everything.

The old man took his hat off, pretended to trample it into the ground with rage, then put it back on his head:

"Well, if I haven't told 'em a thousand times: Good citizens, bring 'em here, to th' village, to th' town hall, for th' mayor t' deal with... Bring 'em here t' me at home, if it's a hardship for you takin' 'em to th' station at Vatici. I may's well be talkin' to meself. After they've approp'iated th' property o' th' state for theirselves - th' parachutes 'ave got t' be handed over to th' state for a receipt, like th' weapons, th' gadgets, th' maps - our folk, scoundrels that they are, take ever'thing, strip 'em raw! Like yest'day, with them two..."

I saw it all, from here, from the *calidor*. Old Iacob was walking along the back lane in front of them, stopping from time to time, beckoning to them over his shoulder and saying:

"*Idite! Idite!*"

Two men in their shirts and underpants. With cropped hair. And nothing on their feet. All three went into the courtyard at the side. Old Iacob pointed to the wooden bench near the wall of the serai: "*Sidite! Sidite!*"

The two razor-cuts sat down. With their hands on their knees. Their faces were dirty, their hands were dirty, their legs were bare and black.

Old Iacob came out of the house followed by Aunt

Domnica. The old woman filled two bowls, ladling out of the big pot, and passed them over to Old Iacob. He held the bowls out to the razor-cuts along with a hunk of bread:

"*Cushite! Cushite! Harasho! Cushite!*"

My Old Iacob was brilliant: he could speak Russian! The Russians looked at each other, then both looked into the other one's bowl, and then they set about bolting it down. After a while, Old Iacob said:

"But take th' bread as well, lads! *Hleba, Hleba!*" - and he pointed to the bread the razor-cuts had in their hands.

The razor-cuts nodded their cropped heads, laughed a little bit, but continued to eat the borsch by itself, each holding his hunk of bread tightly to the bottom of the bowl.

"Diff'rent people, diff'rent pleasures," said Aunt Domnica, ready with the ladle. "Perhaps they're savin' their black bread for blacker days t' come..."

"*Harasho?*" Old Iacob asked them. "*Harasho, cushania?*"

The Russians didn't say a word, their mouths were full. They nodded their pates - those dirty as well - to say yes, it was *harasho cushania*. And stuffed it down. Aunt Domnica filled their bowls again. And again. The pot was empty now, she scraped the ladle against the side and shrugged her shoulders:

"A little from us, a lot from God."

"*Spasiba, spasiba!*" the Russians said quickly, with their mouths full. "*Spasiba!*"

"*Cushite, spasiba,*" Aunt Domnica said. "*Cushite* for *spasiba!*"

"*Spasiba* for *cushite,*" Old Iacob corrected her. "Because it was *harasho - spasiba*'s when he thanks you."

"In that case, *spasiba* for *spasiba!*" Aunt Domnica laughed toothlessly.

"*Spasiba, spasiba!*" the Russians laughed, nodding their heads and showing their really white teeth.

Old Iacob whispered something to his wife, then got out

his cigarette case, the silver one - and held it out to them:
"*Tabachiok! Curite, curite!*"

The Russians laughed even whiter and even wider. They wiped their hands front and back on their underpants before they took a cigarette. Old Iacob gave them a light, then went into the house.

From my place I could see the Russians sitting there alone. One of them looked as if he heaved a sigh, or perhaps he was just blowing out the smoke from his cigarette. Whatever, he nudged the other one and nodded towards the fence and beyond, to the back lane. The other one looked towards the back lane for a bit, sighed as well, then shook his head slowly, as if to say no. And they sat there quite calmly on the bench, calmer than they'd been when the others were around.

Old Iacob came back out of the house with two packets of Nationals and a box of matches for each of them. The Russians "*spasiba*-ed" with lit cigarettes in their mouths and looked for somewhere to put the packets, but they didn't find...

"Go an' get yerself back there again, woman!" shouted Old Iacob.

Aunt Domnica left the house, crossed the stile into our house, but she didn't come in through the front, she came in through the back door - I could hear her talking to Mother in the kitchen, but I couldn't make out what they were saying. After a while, she left the house through the front door, beside me, and crossed back over with some clothes over her arm.

Now the strangers weren't total strangers any more: one of them was wearing a pair of Father's trousers, the other one was wearing one of Father's jackets.

"That's all I've got, Old Iacob," said Mother, coming to where I was on the *calidor*. "I mean, I've got other things but my husband will be coming back - he's got to have something to put on, hasn't he?"

160

After Old Iacob had given the one wearing Father's jacket a pair of trousers and the one wearing Father's trousers a flannel shirt, the gendarmes arrived. Led by their boss, Grabenko.

"Come on into the house!" Mother said hurriedly.

"But I want to see!"

"There's nothing for you to see!" and she picked me up, blankets and all, and carried me into the house. "You'd be better off seeing how your pins are getting along..."

That's what Mother called my legs, which were covered in horrible spots below the knees - because of them I couldn't walk, couldn't bend my knees, because of them I couldn't go down to join in the games. I'd caught them when I was paddling - so Mother said. Perhaps.

Because my pins were sick I was lying on the *calidor* wrapped in blankets up to my waist. After lessons, Mother went to Vatici. To get the doctor, because my pins weren't getting any better.

Today they didn't drop. The parachutes. Perhaps they're not ever going to come down again - the day before yesterday there were loads of them, I counted two hundred alone. Well, twenty. There were so many of them, but I only managed to count twelve. Mind you, I'm not sure whether I counted some of them twice.

Yesterday they didn't drop. At this time yesterday it was all happening with the *devoushka*.

I was lying on the *calidor*. From the back of his house, I could hear the familiar voice of Old Iacob. Calling for Aunt Domnica - but not in his usual way, for all the village to hear - in an unusual way; as if he'd got caught in a nettle patch and couldn't get out again. I could see the old woman running away from the house. And wailing - but quietly, as well. After a short while, I saw her coming back, still running, and holding a black shawl in front of her mouth - it looked like the old woman was laughing but I wasn't sure. She crossed the stile into our house and, as usual, snagged her dress - if not herself as well: she went around in dresses that touched the ground... Mother, who'd come out onto the *calidor*, asked what had happened.

"What's 'appened? Lord, I've lived t' see even this!" - Aunt Domnica had freed herself from the stile and came towards us. "The scoundrels they are in Mana: they took absolutely everything, left 'er in 'er bare skin..."

"Who?" asked Mother.

"A young girl. They're even sendin' us young girls now, th' pagans!"

"Who's sending what?" Mother didn't understand (neither did I).

"Them Russian pagans! Tyin' up young girls in th' parachutes! An' they send 'em here! An' those Mana scoundrels - that Morcov, the villain - 'ave taken all 'er things, everything, an' left 'er just as 'er mother made 'er - an' where? In th' middle of th' thicket at Curchi, where th' mosquitoes an' leeches 'ave feasted on 'er - p'rhaps you've got some clothes, for th' young thing..."

"Of course I have," Mother said. "Bring her here!"

"I'll bring 'er, but round th' back, so people don't see. My Iacob wrapped 'er up in a jacket of 'is, yes, really! But it doesn't cover 'er up everywhere..."

"Bring her around the back way!"

I was lying on the *calidor*, looking straight in front of me, but my ear was cocked towards the back, where the window near the hall had been left open and the kitchen door was ajar - that's where they'd taken her. I had asked if I could see the young girl as well. Mother said I had to wait for a bit, she was having a little wash. And so I waited. With Old Iacob.

The old man was wandering around our courtyard, smoking and muttering about the scoundrels of Mana - who didn't respect the law. Mother and Aunt Domnica came out onto the *calidor*.

"What if she runs away, through th' back?" the old

woman whispered.

"She won't run away," Mother said.

"Where's she goin' to run to?" - Old Iacob joined in. "Back there, to th' thicket? Into th' forest? Th' gendarmes'll catch 'er. Or our Mana folk - which's even worse... This way, th' journey's shorter, she'll end up in th' camp in any case..."

He stepped up onto the *calidor* and started telling his story:

"When she saw me, you know how she came over t' me? As if I was 'er own dad... Like this, with 'er arms reachin' out an' tears on 'er cheeks..."

"What, there in th' thicket?" Aunt Domnica asked with a sidelong glance.

"Where else? When I heard that Morcov 'ad caught a girl, I said t' myself: he'll be keepin' 'er fer himself... I'll not say any more, th' young boy's here... I went t' see 'im at 'is nest an' said: where's th' girl? Get th' girl out, or you'll rot away in jail! He started twitterin' on: what girl, I've only got boys! Lord, I belted 'im one an' said: Get th' girl out! He said: I let 'er go, what was I t' do with 'er? I've got the wife here as well... How did you let 'er go? I said. An' where? I said. An' I said, Tell me lies an' you'll be straight for court martial - get th' girl out! He said: But I let 'er go, last night, or th' night before even, when she came down - she fell straight into my arms, so I helped 'er to the edge o' the forest an' id *Davai!* Get yerself as far away from 'ere as possible. I belted 'im one again. What was she wearin'? I said. He said: Well, y'know, she wasn't wearin' all that much, I mean, she wasn't really wearin' anythin' - who knows what scoundrel had got 'is hands on 'er an' taken all 'er clothes... I said: But you said she fell straight in yer arms, that you took 'er out o' th' harness - she was naked in th' harness, was she? So you see, I don't know what... I said, I'll settle with you later about th' clothes an' th' state's property, but now let's find 'er! An' for a while both of us looked for 'er, shoutin' *Devoushka! Devoushka!* - 'cause that's what they call young

163

girls in their language... An' then I realised I was shoutin' by myself, Morcov 'ad run off - but just wait 'til I get my hands on 'im... I looked for 'er by myself, shoutin' *Devoushka! Devoushka!* An' straight away I saw 'er... Look you, woman, go an' get some o' that medicinal vinegar o' yours, th' mosquitoes and leeches 'ave murdered 'er!"

"I'll go, I'll go an' get it, long as we've got time - 'ave you sent for that 'cursed Grabenko?"

"I've sent word - but 'til 'e comes..."

Until the accursed boss of the station came, we all waited at our house, in the drawing room. The *devoushka* wasn't really like a young girl; the dress that Mother had given her was too tight everywhere, the hooks above her hips wouldn't even fasten, it wouldn't go around her, you could see her skin. Perhaps she was swollen from the mosquitoes, poor girl, that was why she was so big. Her hair was wet, she was combing it now. Her cheeks were really big and her eyes were really small - perhaps that was because of the mosquitoes as well. Mother gave her something to eat.

"*Cushite! Cushite! Harasho!*" Old Iacob urged her.

"It would be better if she'd 'cush' more quickly and you took her away from here," said Mother. "I don't want that swine-Grabenko to set foot in my house."

The *devoushka* was eating, but not with the same appetite as the razor-cuts did.

"I'll go and look for something else for her to wear," said Mother. "Something warmer, the winter's coming, poor girl..."

She left the drawing room; we all stayed behind.

"Why don't you ask 'er 'ow old she is?" Aunt Domnica said to her husband.

Old Iacob coughed, scratched his head for inspiration and said:

"*Devoushka! Let? Let?*" - and wiggled and waved his fingers in front of the *devoushka's* face. "*Skolko? Skolko?*"

The *devoushka* understood. She laughed - pleased - and

said something in her language. This time, we didn't understand. The *devoushka* counted out on her fingers.

"Are you listenin'? She says nineteen!" Old Iacob translated.

"I got that. We can count on our fingers as well you know. Ask 'er if she's married."

Old Iacob started scratching his head again. He gave a long cough, as if preparing himself for a lengthy speech, and wriggled about on the seat. Then he arrived at a decision: he showed the *devoushka* his third finger, with the wedding ring on it. The *devoushka* leaned forward, looked at it carefully, stretched out her hand and touched it...

"Are-you-married-where-you-come-from?" Old Iacob asked.

"Even I understand that Russian!" Aunt Domnica said.

"Shut up! Y' married, *devoushka* ?"

"*Shto?*" the *devoushka* said, laughing.

"You got a husband - *esti*?" Old Iacob persisted. "Husband! Wedding - *esti*?" and he pointed to his wedding ring finger again, then reached forward to take her hand...

"*Oi!*" the *devoushka* shrieked, pulling her hand away and hiding it behind her back - and laughing.

"She mustn't realise what you're pointing at," said Mother, who'd returned in the meantime with a pile of clothes. "She must think you're asking her where her wedding ring is - if she's married, that is."

"Or if she knows what a weddin' ring is!" said Aunt Domnica.

"*Devoushka!*" Old Iacob tried again. "Is there an *esti...esti*, 'ave you got a *ciolovec*?" and he waved his hands in front of the Russian girl's face.

"*Celaviek?*" the *devoushka* said. Then, after she'd thought for a while, she started counting on her fingers.

"She hasn't understood," said Mother. "She's counted up to twelve, she thinks you're asking how many came down in the parachutes."

"Well, I think she's showin' 'ow many men she's..."

Aunt Domnica covered her mouth with the shawl; Mother shouted at her and pointed to me - I shouldn't hear.

"If you think th' boy doesn't know about that kind o' thing..." Old Iacob ventured, but Mother said:

"Old Iacob! He's my son, it's up to me what he should know and what he shouldn't!"

Then she changed the subject and said to the girl,

"Look, *devoushka*, take this as well... And this ... and look, these as well - this is for when it's cold, brr!" - and Mother shivered really convincingly. "And this is for..."

For what? Mother had sat down in front of her with her back to me, so that I couldn't see what she was showing her. She leant towards her, whispered something to her - in Romanian, what knowledge did she have of Russian? I saw the *devoushka's* shoulders shrugging, as if she didn't understand. Mother took things from the very beginning and started showing her...

"An' what else does baldie need, a tit strap!" Aunt Domnica giggled.

"Aunt Domnica!" Mother shouted, spinning around quickly - which gave me the opportunity to see what was going on. "The child!"

"If you think th' boy doesn't know what that is...," giggled Old Iacob. "The boy knows, but look, the *devoushka* doesn't..."

"Good Lord!" Mother exclaimed and sat down again between me and the Russian girl. "But not like that, really girl, you don't put it on outside, you wear it inside..."

It was pointless Mother trying to stop me from seeing, I'd seen: the *devoushka* had put her bra on top of her dress. When she understood eventually that it wasn't done like that, she stuffed it down the front of her dress. She looked at Mother again, to see whether she'd done it right this time.

"You'll see, she'll blow 'er nose on it next," the old woman said.

"It'd be better if you shut up," Old Iacob said. "What d'you know about those things anyway? 'Ave you worn one? You never!"

"How could I 'ave, if you never brought me one? If you'd brought me one, from th' market in town... But at least I know what they're for, an' 'ow you put 'em on..."

"Listen!" Old Iacob shook, and jumped up in a hurry. "The gendarmes!"

"Go out the back way, so that swine of a Grabenko doesn't come into my house!" said Mother. "You wait a little bit, *devoushka*, and I'll give you a packet of cotton wool," and she ran into her room, then came back. "Look, this is for... Come over here and I'll explain, I'll show you..."

All four of them went out through the back, I stayed in the drawing room. Alone. The smell of the *devoushka* was still there. A mixture of Mother's soap and something else - it wasn't anything horrible, but strange. They'd said that she'd be put into the camp as well - in the same one as Father?

Outside, I could hear many voices - in front, in the courtyard. Mother returned through the *calidor*.

"What did the *devoushka* need cotton wool for?" I asked her. "Has she got spots on her pins as well? From paddling?"

"Hm-hmmm!" said Mother, looking in the other direction.

Knocks at the door. Mother rushed forward, double-locked it, then asked very loudly: "Who is it?"

"The station chief, Madam. Open up!"

"Say what you've got to say through the door."

"I've got something to say and I've got something to give you as well. I've brought you your clothes back."

"Whaaat?" - Mother unlocked the door immediately and opened it wide. "Why have you brought them back? What did you take them from her for? I gave them to her, they're hers now!"

167

"Where she's going she doesn't need them, the State takes care of clothes for ladies. True, we don't cater for these things..."

I couldn't see what he was pointing at, but I found out when Mother furiously snatched the bra out of his hand. A second later, she took the bundle of clothes. She slammed the door and locked it twice.

Knocks at the door again.

"What do you want? What do you want this time?"

"I've brought you your cotton wool back as well," said the gendarme outside. "You're throwing pearls before swine, Madam. I asked her if she knew what it was for. She said she knew, it was used for bandaging wounds - the Russians are savages, Madam, they haven't got a clue about..."

"But aren't you Russian as well?" shouted Mother, on the brink of tears.

"You're making a mistake, Madam. I'm Ukrainian."

"But isn't that the same?"

"No, Madam. And the proof of the pudding is that I know what cotton wool is used for..."

"Well, in that case, give it to your wife - if you know what it's for!"

"Thanks a lot. Actually, I was even going to ask you..."

"All right, all right, take it and go away! Good night!"

"Good night, and I hope you won't pull another one like this. We're at war, there isn't even enough cotton wool for our wounded, Romanian wounded - and you... Really, it's even debatable whether you should be allowed to have it for your own personal use..."

"My own personal use has got nothing to do with you!" Mother shouted.

"...but it has when it's for a Russian sow, parachuted in to sabotage us, to give us all kinds of..."

"Don't you try and lecture me! Good riddance to you!"

Mother put the clothes on a chair and sat down on another one at the table, her head in her hands. I thought she was crying.

"Why are you crying, Mother? Are you crying because of the Russian sow?"

I had hardly got the words out of my mouth when Mother gave me the most terrible smack.

"Why are you hitting me?" I howled. "Can't you see I'm ill? And a little orphan?"

"You'll get more of where that came from if I hear any more of that filth!"

"But I didn't say it, the station chief said it!"

"And what are you repeating that swine's filth for?"

"I wasn't repeating it! I only asked you why you were crying - and you..."

"But I wasn't crying, my darling, where on earth did you get that idea?" said Mother, smiling and wiping away her tears. "Can't you tell how happy I am?"

"I can. But I'll be able to tell even better if you tell me what the cotton wool's all about."

"But I told you: when you're wounded..."

"The *devoushka* wasn't wounded, I never saw her wound..."

"Just as well you didn't. Anyway, come on, off to bed!"

I'm Not an Orphan Any More...

I was lying on the *calidor* waiting for the parachutes to come down over the forest. And because the parachutes didn't appear, I waited for Mother who'd gone to Vatici to get the doctor, for my pins.

But Mother didn't appear either - or she hadn't yet anyway. However, a stranger appeared at the little gate. He didn't knock. The gate opened and a man I didn't know came into the courtyard.

I said to myself: A parachutist! He's managed to land somewhere where Morcov wasn't waiting to take his clothes from him: not only did this man have clothes on, but he was wearing shoes as well. Perhaps he'd found out (I don't know where from) that the best thing to do was to hand yourself over to Old Iacob...

"*Idite, idite!*" I shouted to him, and pointed over the fence to Old Iacob's courtyard next door and to the seat on the serai wall where the razor-cuts had been sitting. "*Sidite, sidite!*" I urged him.

The stranger understood what I was saying - I was speaking Russian, you see! But there was something else he didn't understand. Something, I don't know what. And he said - but in Romanian:

"You don't know me any more..."

A-ha, he wasn't a parachutist, he was a Romanian.

"Who are you looking for?" I asked him, the way people did around here when a stranger came into their courtyard.

"I am... You don't recognise me any more...," the stranger said sadly and humbly, and as if he was afraid that I'd set the dog on him if he didn't leave as quickly as he'd come in.

170

Well, as if he was... Well, yes. Yes.

The man with snow-white hair was dressed in a white short-sleeved shirt, which I recognised, and black moleskin trousers. I recognised the trousers as well, although they didn't lie right without the familiar black, shiny, knee boots with the sparkling, jingling spurs; the trousers didn't lie right with that kind of knee boot (I say knee boot, because they came up knee-high), which didn't seem to be made out of leather, but seemed like canvas and they weren't black either, the canvas was khaki - the man who was crossing the courtyard and approaching the *calidor*, hesitantly and with trembling, tight lips, was Father.

He had come back.

He embraced me in tears; I embraced him sobbing. However, I was crying for another reason as well: this Father didn't smell like the other Father, the one I'd forgotten. And then I cried because, that was it, I wasn't a little orphan any more. Until now, I'd heard, "Teacher-Sir's boy, the poor little mite...," and Teacher-Sir was poor as well because the Russians had pulled him in and me as well because I was Teacher-Sir's boy, left a little orphan. Poor mite. Until now everybody had pitied me, spoiled me, forgiven all my pranks, the women and girls had told me not to tell anyone when I looked up there, and if a stranger didn't know who I was, I told them: "I am the son of the headmaster who the Russians pulled in, poor man..." - and so both of us were poor, Father and me. But especially me.

Mother came back as well, from Vatici - without the doctor, but with new ointments and powders for my pins, although I didn't need them any more, I'd stood up by myself and walked; Old Iacob and Aunt Domnica came to our house as well, and the neighbours came and the not-so-near neighbours, the whole village came. And a devil-of-a-party began, this time because of joy. They were drinking, singing, cheering and shouting and once again drinking, singing and cheering...

I sat on the *calidor*. Waiting for them to come back from the cemetery. Everybody had gone to the cemetery, with spades and shovels and bottles of wine. Singing like during a wedding and crooning like after a wedding. I could hear them cheering and warbling over there, and down here on their way back.

Look at Father: he was carrying the oak cross on his back, which had been dug out of the cemetery from beside my little brother Peter's little stone cross. I thought I'd seen something like this before in a book. But in the book, the man carrying the cross wasn't as happy; and his hair wasn't falling into his eyes and his eyes weren't glazed with drink either; and the people accompanying him weren't as happy or as drunk or as noisy either. And some people had beaten the other man - nobody was hitting Father. In the book, Father didn't slam the cross down in the middle of the courtyard and he didn't smash it up with an axe; he didn't pour petrol on it and set it alight. And he didn't dance, naked down to the waist, with Russian boots on made out of khaki tent-canvas; and he didn't take the Russian canvas boots off and hurl them into the fire, one after the other, on top of the cross; and he didn't bellow, dancing naked, barefoot, with a bottle of wine in his hand and with his hair in his eyes and with his eyes glazed over.

The grown-ups were villains, scoundrels - Old Iacob too, and Father was their leader. Why had they ruined that lovely cross made out of solid oak and carved by Old Iacob, really nicely - and I'd worked on it as well. Wasn't I the one who'd given him a hand, passing him one chisel or another, or the divider, or whichever tool he needed?

"Scoundrels! You're all villains and scoundrels!" I cried from my perch.

Only Old Iacob took any notice of me. He was stung as well, a little bit. He came up to sit beside me and asked me why I was crying, were the spots on my legs hurting?

172

"The soul in my heart's hurting!", I bellowed, pleased that now I had someone to listen to me. "You've ruined the beau-ti-ful cross! And I worked so hard on it!"

"Is that why you're cryin'? Thank the Lord for th' chance o' breakin' it, my littl' lad," Old Iacob said. "You're a big boy now, you can read - can you remember what we both wrote on th' cross? Wi' the chisel? You know: the hook!"

How could I not remember? Mother had come over to Old Iacob's when the cross was still on the chocks, in the serai, and had said:

"Heavens, Old Iacob, you've made a mistake with the year of death, you've written 1991 instead of 1941 - but look, you've done it in cubic numerals, you can just break the top off the 9 and make it into a 4..."

And laughing, Old Iacob had said,

"But I've made no mistake, Missus, that's the hook! War's just begun, our boys haven't liberated all th' prisons an' Russian camps yet - an' what if, today-or-tomorrow, Teacher-Sir comes back? An' sees 'is own grave? An' on th' cross, 1941 as 'is time of dyin'? Wouldn't 'e die of a bad heart there an' then? Like a brother-in-law o' mine, Domnica's brother, 'e came back from th' Great War, from th' Germans, from a prison, an' when 'e saw that 'is wife 'ad buried 'im an' put a cross up, wi' th' date of 'is death all marked up three-years-past... Wha'd'e do? What could he do? He lied straight down an' died! Of a bad heart. But us, wi' this little hook of ours we'll catch Teacher-Sir an' reel 'im back to home - wherever 'e might be!"

And there you go, he did reel him in. With the hook. But surely Father couldn't be reeled in any further without breaking the hook? Without being pulled into the fire and getting burned? Without dancing round it, like a savage in the savageness of the savage jungle? And without shouting *Long Live Gutenberg!*? He'd danced once before and had ended up in Siberia!

And there was that swine Grabenko.

173

"Here we are, drinking and dancing, enjoying ourselves, while our Romanian soldiers are shedding their blood for our Motherland, at the front..."

On this occasion, I *asked* Mother to take me into the house.

I was sitting on the *calidor* of the house in Mana and was shaking. Shaking with sadness, out of pity for myself: the parachutes didn't come down for me; and when they did come down it would have been better if they hadn't. Either once they touched the tops of the trees, or the ground, they rushed to hand themselves over; or the opposite. Like now.

It would have been better if they'd gone straight to the station, at Vatici, much better again to hand themselves straight over to that swine Grabenko, than this. Of course, the best thing was to hand yourself over to Old Iacob, so we could speak Russian. But this way...

I was shaking with the cold and out of sadness: I wasn't a little orphan any more. By coming home, Father had abandoned me.

And so I sat on the *calidor*. Alone. And shaking. I had plenty of clothes on, boots lined with sheepskin and a fur cap pulled down over my ears - but I was still shaking because of the cold today.

In the middle of the courtyard, where last autumn there'd been the Bonfire of the Cross and many years ago there'd been the Bonfire of the Books - a worthy fire was blazing, with worthy pieces of wood, and which was worthily melting the snow around it. It had become dark quite some time earlier and Mother had tired of calling for me to come into the house; later she didn't really want me in the house, and I didn't really want to go in either, it wasn't like our house today. I knew that Father was blind-drunk in the kitchen; I knew that the swine Grabenko had shut himself away in the drawing room with a little officer. And with maps and little books and pieces of paper. I wished Grabenko would go to

174

hell - but not the little officer.

In the courtyard, Old Iacob was keeping the fire going and handing wine out to the soldiers. The soldiers were a bit older than the ones who'd looked for Father in the trees - but were soldiers just the same. But not soldiers of mine. Aunt Domnica was mulling the wine in our kitchen. With sugar, cinnamon and black pepper, of ours - the wine was theirs. The soldiers were slurping out of metal cups, flattened and bent, as if they weren't properly finished, but that's how they'd come from the factory. They slurped and said very little. Old Iacob walked to and fro among the soldiers, pouring them mulled wine out of our big teapot.

He didn't give any wine to the two who were lying on the snow to the left of the fire. He didn't give them anything. He didn't give anything to the ones spread out at the right side of the fire either, the five of them, even though he kept stopping in front of them and talking to them - sometimes in Romanian, other times in his kind of Russian. As he stood talking to them, Old Iacob sucked on the teapot spout and then spat out a little bit of red wine on to the snow. Violet. Black. Then he went into the kitchen and came back with the teapot, and honoured everyone with a drink, and of course himself...

Aunt Domnica came out to tell me that the chicken in sauce was already cooked on the stove and that if I didn't come in that very minute, Grabenko would eat it. I wasn't hungry, but when I heard that the swine Grabenko...

It was really crowded in the kitchen. I had to take my boots off and climb up onto the shelf above the stove. Mother was busy at the kitchen range with the food; Aunt Domnica with the wine; Father, at the table with the brandy. He was sitting as stiff as a board on the seat, his eyes were colourless, the muscles of his cheeks were twitching all the time, which meant that he was really annoyed; or very drunk.

The chief of the station opened the kitchen door. He had a long fur coat over his shoulders and a fur cap on his head -

175

although I knew he'd only come through from the drawing room. He said to Father, "There's no point mourning for them, Headmaster, you can't bring them back!" - and made to slap him on the shoulder as friends do.

Father's glazed eyes glared and he batted the approaching hand away from him and swore at him. In Romanian and in Russian, he called him *svoloci* and *hohol*; and something about *stuchinsin* - Old Iacob said that was a terrible swear-word in Russian, but I couldn't understand why, shitting wasn't nice, but it wasn't swearing either - anyway it was something you did by yourself, not on anybody else.

While he was still grumbling at the station chief - who wasn't taking any notice of him - Father filled two mugs with brandy. He drank his without making a toast, Grabenko picked the other one up, drank it, laughed - and left. I heard him go outside into the courtyard.

Somebody knocked at the door. It was the little officer. He was very young and had only one hand. He stopped in the doorway and asked if he was bothering anyone. Of course not! everyone replied. Aunt Domnica took him by his empty sleeve and led him to the table, in front of Father. Mother put a mug of tea in front of him.

"To hell with the tea!" Father said. "He's drinking brandy. To help you forget..."

"Thank you, but you know: when I drink it's even..."

Father must have known what he meant, he didn't insist. I knew a little something as well: the little officer had been to our house before, twice - always with... The snow hadn't fallen the first time. But snow or not, it had been all right those two times because it had been in vain, and he and his soldiers had returned from the forest empty-handed (or with one empty hand). But this time...

Father was singing and beating time on the table with his glass which was spilling everywhere. He was singing a carol. He was making signs for us to come in with the chorus: "*Lord, Lord, raise up our hearts!*" - but we didn't feel like it. He sang alone:

"*They've gone out hunting,/ Lord, Lord, raise up our hearts,/ To hunt down kids,/ Lord, Lord, raise up...* - have you gone hunting kids as well, Mr Hunter?"

I knew that the little officer had been a hunter. A mountain hunter, they said. I knew what mountains were, but I'd never seen any. Mountain hunters were hunters who hunted in the mountains - and wore berets. The little officer didn't wear his beret any more because he'd been drafted to this - so I'd heard. Drafting is when you're wounded and in the hospital they cut off your hand and then send you home, but afterwards take you from your home again and draft you. To this, I mean to Mana, in the forests, with the old soldiers. But hunting all the same - or at least just now he'd been hunting.

The little officer couldn't stop nodding his head, yes, over the cups of teas. A bit later he stopped and held two fingers out.

Aunt Domnica looked at the number of fingers, made the sign of the cross and covered her face up even more with her black shawl - you couldn't tell whether she was crying or praying underneath.

"You've been there with them, you know what they're like," the little officer said. "Why do they send them here? Surely they know - or they should know - that it's pointless, ninety percent of them hand themselves over. Even if not straight away... Fair enough, in the last month they haven't all handed themselves over, some of them have resisted - but what's the good? They last as long as they can in the heart of the forest, in the caves, on the hillsides, with no way out... Why do they send them to certain death?"

"Why!" Father said. "That's just why!"

"That's it: that's just why," the officer smiled sadly. "Mind you, our leaders have made...still make some mistakes - let's not go into details - but *them*... You'd think it was tactics - do you know what maps the ones today had with them?"

"I don't know, but I can guess," said Father. "Let's say the Odorhei region, which they'd confused with Orhei - what does it matter to them, a two or three hundred kilometre diversion? They wouldn't even have heard that Odorhei is in Northern Transylvania and that the Hungarians took it some three years ago..."

"Worse than that," the little officer said. "This was a diversion of more than 700 kilometres. They should have been parachuted down into the Zvolen, in Slovakia..."

"What did I tell you! The Russian says: *Vseo ravno*..."

"What does that mean?"

"That means ... anywhere, as long as it's straight ahead, *vperiod*..."

"Yes, but all the same..."

"You don't understand, do you, Lieutenant? The Russians don't think Yes-but-all-the-same. They sent them ... for sending them's sake, they have 'plans for sending' to carry out. And if at the aerodrome the maps got mixed up or even the planes - so what?"

"That's why the ones last week had maps of Eastern Prussia - is that how they think they're going to win the war?"

Father patted him on the back, and made a sign to him that he wanted to say something in his ear. And he whispered - but loudly:

"That's it! It's just like that! They're steam-rolling them in! They're bursting with people - where we count men, they count divisions! Let's have a drink! And forget - *For only for-get-ting*..." - but that was as much of the song as Father knew.

Mother gave him a dirty look and made a sign - for him to stop drinking. Father shrugged his shoulders.

"You were saying that you've also hunted ... kids? Really? To the very end?" - the officer nodded from time to time. "Who was behind it: the great-Romanian Grabenko?"

178

- the officer nodded again. "And then the usual, after the little kids come in, all alone and by themselves, to eat from his hand?"

"Only one came," the officer sighed. "The other one had a bullet in her spine, and they said she couldn't be moved..."

"She said she couldn't be moved? What do the Russians call that, the...?"

"She didn't say so. He did ... he said what was the point in even... But it's happened to me as well, two boys... One of them had escaped from Stalingrad and look where he ended up dying..."

"God rest their souls, all of the boys and the little girls!" Father said and started drinking from the bottle - then he turned to Grabenko, who'd just come in again: "So tell me, you've shot a little Russian girl as well!"

"Not a Russian girl - a *bolshevik*, you Bolshevik!" the gendarme laughed.

"Did you give her a good search? She wasn't one of your Ukrainians, was she, *hohol*?"

"There are no such things as Russians and Ukrainians in my book..."

"You don't have to swear on it, I believe you! In your mentality people are divided into bolsheviks and anti-bolsheviks - there is no middle road!"

"You see, you've learned the lesson, Bolshevik!" Grabenko smirked. "What is it, are you sorry you've had nobody to translate for today? Don't worry, once I get my hands on the others, I'll call you in to translate for me..."

"Not for you!" Father said. "But for them, I'll even translate the orders I've received direct from Moscow."

"You see, you have learned the lesson, haven't you? We'll continue our discussion another time. We've got to go now, Lieutenant, our sleighs have arrived. Sorry for the inconvenience, Madam..."

"I hadn't even noticed you were here," Mother said. "Not surprising if you keep yourself hidden under that fur cap - do you walk around with your hat on in your own house? And what does your wife have to say about it?"

"Sorry, Madam, we were just about to go..." the chief took his fur cap off: "Come on, Lieutenant, good-bye Madam..."

"And good riddance, and regards to your wife," Mother said. "Has she still got some cotton wool for her personal use?"

"Well, as a matter of fact, not really... But don't worry about that now, I'll pop in another..."

"What's the point of popping in, just get your hands on another young bolshevik woman, bring her here, I'll give her some cotton wool, you shoot her, nicely though, and take her..."

"Cut it out, Madam, it wasn't quite like that - let's go - *now*, Lieutenant!"

And they left. Off they went ... Father even showed them the way to go. Later, much later, Father said:

"When I built the school in Mana, at one particular time I needed more waggoners than were available in the village, and he sent them to me from another place. From then on I couldn't get rid of him, he was eager for ... intellectual discussion... Your mother couldn't stand him at all. And she told him so. In '40, he was among the first wave of people to become refugees, in '41 I found out he was one of the first to come back - a gendarme always does his duty... In '43, when they freed me from the camp at Slobozia - although I'd been immediately reinstated in my position in education - I had to present myself weekly at the station, to sign on. Normal - it was the war, I was an ex-Soviet prisoner, the front was moving back, the Russians were sending parachutists... But if I really had been a danger to the security of the State, the State would have kept me ... in security in the camp, wouldn't it? That's what everybody thought, and they looked upon me as exactly what I was: a victim of the Soviets - everybody did, apart from my 'friend' Grabenko... He was convinced that I'd been sent on a mission from Moscow... So I had to present myself at the station every week for two months - then he called me in right up to the day of my leaving as a refugee for my mother's at Ciocalteni and my parents-in-law's at Chistelnita. First he delayed my departure, then he accompanied me there - at my expense... And when he got his hands on a parachutist, he would call me in to Vatici to translate ... I went the first time, and the second, but not the third.

"He came to Mana: 'Why aren't you carrying out your orders, Headmaster?' I told him I wasn't under his command; his knowledge of Russian was much better, he *was* a Russian! and I wasn't even obliged to him. 'You're just afraid I'll uncover who and what you are,' he said. I told him that there was nothing for him to uncover, firstly I'd been screened by the Gestapo; then by the SS, and after that by State Security - if there was something to find out surely they would have uncovered it, they wouldn't have waited for the station chief at Vatici to do so, would they? But he wanted to know - from me! - all about this Russian 'trick' of sending us parachutes with maps of only-the-devil-knows-where in Slovakia and Prussia, it had to be some kind of 'strategy'... I said: 'You mean: tragedy...' and I told him what I believed, based on the little I knew - that the Russians were sending parachutists, for sending-them's sake... He didn't believe me, was always spying on me, and when he organised the 'hunts' in the surrounding areas, he did his bit, then brought the 'game' back to Mana into the schoolyard, I just might have given myself away as being sent by the Soviets on a mission..."

Even later on, Father said:

"Just look at this history of ours! Or at how it's made; or at how the Devil is making it while God's picking his nose or sleeping... I think it was in '62, I was coming back from seeing you in Baragan, I had to change at Brasov and I went to a restaurant to get something to eat - and who do you think was there? Grabenko! We had a drink together, he told me he'd just retired, I told him what had been happening over the last near-on twenty years: the flight, the running away to the forest in the autumn of '44, the 'repatriation' we'd escaped, our arrests in '49, yours in '52, and then in '56 - in the end, I told him I'd just come back from seeing you, in Baragan, where your 'obligatory residence' was...

"Grabenko listened attentively - he was interested. And he nodded, compassionately. Then he said, 'Why didn't you look for me, old friend, I could have helped you out...' I said, 'What help? Nobody could have helped me...' However he stuck to what he'd said, why hadn't I looked for him? 'I'd just got rid of you - what would I come and look for you for?' I said. But he said: 'Ttt! But if I'd known what trouble you were in, I could have given you a recommendation in some sense or other!' 'Some sense or other - in what sense?' I asked. 'To the effect that, during the anti-Soviet criminal war, you were very active in operations behind the front...'

"I choked on my food: 'What are you talking about? Which front? I wasn't active behind any front!' 'Look here, Headmaster, I mean, where was I when I was with the Soviet partisans, if I wasn't right in the middle of it all? I would have given you a recommendation in the sense that you too were connected with them!'

"I stared at him to try and see whether he was joking - he didn't seem to have turned comedian since I'd last seen him. I said, 'Connected with what? You even saw my dossier, there's no way you couldn't have realised that I wasn't connected with...'

" 'Listen, Headmaster, I'm not talking about what really happened - I mean, if you'd really been working with them, they wouldn't have paid you as much attention as they did, but you would have been decorated and received a good position - I'm referring to the recommendation now: I would have given it to you there on the spot, to the effect that you

182

were a strong pro-Soviet activist - that's what I mean, I mean we were good friends...'

" 'What...good friends?!'

" 'Well, weren't we? If you'd found me in time, I would have given it to you on the spot - who would have checked it out, huh? Listen, if I said white was white, white it was - things were what I said they were!'

" 'And how on earth, I wonder, would things have *stayed* as you said they were?'

" 'What do you mean, how? Hmm! Well, wasn't I working for them myself?' "

"With them...with whom? With the parachutists? The ones he shot?" I was confused.

Father continued, "Thankfully, my train had arrived, our 'discussion' was interrupted just there. But even if I'd stayed longer, I don't think I'd have asked him who he was working for. Anyway, I didn't feel like sitting talking anymore with a colonel, even if he'd just retired..."

"A colonel. In the Security Service."

"That's what he said. Perhaps he was boasting - only you don't boast in public about those kinds of things. And he didn't look like he'd ever been in prison. If he was a gendarme..."

"He wouldn't have been the first turncoat. I came across some of their kind in prison..."

"Yes, but they ... had to do something, they were thrown in - in prison, that is... Not Grabenko, though. The swine! Not him ... who spied on me, called me bolshevik, the man who blew parachutists' brains out - just look at him now, Colonel in the Securitate! Do you like it?"

I shrugged my shoulders. Of course not - however, I'd heard in prison about so many other turncoats - even more ruthless, like all turncoats who have debts to repay ...

Father shrugged his shoulders as well. And laughed.

"Like it or not, it's sink or swim; we have to sing to His-to-ry's stinking tune... When she gets her eyes on a people, on a group of people, or even on an individual, she doesn't let you out of sight. Do you think you get punished for doing something wrong? That there's even a grain of logic in it? - far from it! When she gets you in her sights...

"Look at my case: so the Russians occupied Basarabia in June of '40; let's say that the fact that we didn't flee in time was half of the trouble - but the other half? What blame was mine - in general? I said to myself: *Me*, the bolsheviks won't do anything to me: I wasn't rich, I wasn't involved in politics, I wasn't a priest or a gendarme. I wasn't, my parents weren't and my parents' parents weren't. What could they have on me? And I was right, for a time they had nothing; they didn't do anything to me ... I looked around me: the higher-level civil servants were pulled in; but I wasn't a high-level civil servant; the landowners, capitalists, bourgies - pulled in; yes, but I didn't fit into those 'categories' either. Then came the turn of the priests, monks, then the turn of the *kulaks* - hey, this might be it... But I said to myself that I, that I might not be a peasant any more, but I wasn't a *kulak* either. I was a teacher and nothing was going to happen to *me*, even the bolsheviks needed teachers...

"But the stench of History lingers around you, watches over you - how could anyone get away scot-free and slip through the net ... of History? Don't the masses make history? I mean, us? And how do we, the masses, make history? This is how: So-and-so, *wasn't he* something or someone? *He might not have been*, but we'll make out - that is, the history made by the masses will make out, *he may have done* something in the past, or *he will do*, in the future... I didn't need to actually *do* anything, I only had to be on the way ... to doing it. Avrum's Sapsa was doing something - it didn't matter that what he was doing was un-doing, destroying, because he was working 'for the development of history': destroying books. And so, the meeting of the meteorite and the Moldavian ox took place, however modest the ox might have been. Do you think that if it wasn't for throwing Sapsa's hat on the ground, I would have got away scot-free? If the incident with his Nogai and his Nagan hadn't happened, events would have passed me by? Or if I hadn't shouted like an idiot, '*Long live Gutenberg!*', His-to-ry would have spared me, overlooked me? Oh no! Only *I* thought I was a nothing, History thought otherwise - and so, through Sapsa, she condemned even me - saying: 'It doesn't matter that you didn't say I was a stinking Jew, it doesn't matter that you didn't cane me until my hands were bleeding; all that matters is that you're a bourgeois teacher - and so, a reactionary; a Romanian - and so, an anti-Semite - because all Romanians are anti-Semitic and all bourgies are reactionary' - full stop. The logic? The truth? The proof? Let's be serious, who's going to haul her in, stinking History, to answer for what she's done, to put her on trial? Like the biggest criminals of our times, they know how to avoid the courts... And so, they pulled *me* in, took me to their place at Orhei and condemned me... Huh! And what did they condemn me for: for anti-Semitism? For forbidden books, for a hidden flag? Because, as a Romanian, I *had to be* bourgeois and reactionary? Hell no, they condemned me for hooliganism! Me, who..."

"But the 'hooliganism' saved your life."

"Yes, but then, at the time, I didn't know that. I thought that from the moment the NKVD bastard started questioning me, I was ... political, wasn't I? When, all of a sudden ... Sapsa looked me straight in the eyes and said, 'You are accused of hooliganism, you've been beating your wife, and you've thrown your son out.' I didn't even begin to think about it, to protest, to ask for evidence - I was already prepared, my head was already shaved. Lawyer, defence, appeal? Let's be serious, nothing stops History on her path forward... Should I have been grateful that somebody who spoke Romanian told me what I'd done, because from Sapsa's place I was taken into another office, where another man grumbled something to me in Russian and wanted me to sign a Russian document. And I signed it, man! Why? Why not! - as go the popular words of wisdom. And if I'd understood what I was signing would it have changed anything? Would I have been set free? Well then...

"From Orhei I was sent to Balta in the Ukraine, where there was a large transit camp. A former Moldavian of ours, a commissary, told me there that I came under common law - I knew that much from Sapsa. In one of the huts I came across some people I knew who told me that I was a lucky beggar, because they, for much less, or even for nothing, had to do ten or fifteen years - but they were political. Sure, later on I was to realise that History, through Sapsa, had been 'kind' to me, but for a time I was utterly unhappy: how was it possible, me a teacher, an educator - and a hooligan? I didn't even tell my colleagues in the carriage, or in the camp, what I'd been condemned for; but there wasn't any need to anyway, in the camp you are what they say you are, not what the guards say you might be... Well..! And so, History had put me on the train and sent me to Vologda, to the 'monastery' - another sorting centre; from there to the canals at Belomorsk; from there to Uhta; after that - the war had started some time before, but we only found out much later - to Arkhangelsk, to unload English ships - heavy crates, armaments... After that, a trip through the *taiga*, cutting down the forests...

"But His-to-ry hadn't forgotten me: one day she sent me another Sapsa, who told me the rest of my sentence had been remitted and that I had been accorded the incredible honour of enrolling in the Red Army! In the meantime I'd learned a little bit of Russian; I had understood what the Sapsa in the *taiga* had said - but I couldn't understand: fair enough, amnesty, reduction in sentence, but the Red Army? Honour? For me, a hooligan? Luckily I didn't have time to ask any questions, in ten minutes the prisoner's rags were changed into the uniform of a *krasnoarmeiets*! They took about one hundred of us from that camp, a thousand from the complex, down to ... somewhere in Kazakhstan. There we met up with thousands of other ... bandits, enemies, hooligans, who'd become brave defenders of the Soviet Motherland, of the beloved Soviet soil... I voiced my surprise quite loudly to one of my 'comrades-in-arms', a Hungarian: 'Well then, how come they've transformed us into exactly the opposite?' 'Keep your mouth shut, or they'll throw you back into the conflict of opposites!' the Hungarian said. Fine ... I've already told you what it was like at the 'front', and how the 'attacks' were carried out. I didn't have time to feel sorry for the Russians, in our units only the commanders and the officers were Russian, but later on, in the camp at Slobozia, I found out that their units were sent to the slaughterhouse as well as us non-Russians... Let's say I was quite surprised that, brave soldiers of the Red Army (which we all were), as soon as they had left their positions (to attack, like at Grivita, with bayonets, shouting 'Hurrah!'), and as soon as they were certain that the Germans hadn't changed their tactics since yesterday, and that again today German artillery would be firing at the rear to cut us all off, they too shot their officers and raised their hands in surrender.

"And so, with my hands in the air - I'd never held my hands up in the air with greater pleasure in my whole life - I waited for the Germans to come and take their spoils ... no surprises here. We were all non-Russians: Polish, Finnish, Baltic, Hungarian, Romanian. It did surprise me, though, the treatment we received from the Germans. Pigs! Even to us, who were all victims of the Russians. They behaved like swine, especially with the Poles. I was blessed by luck; at one stage, I found myself next to a Feldwebel who was getting on a bit, a Saxon from Sibiu; my mouth was going nineteen to the dozen, talking without even being asked a question, half in French, a quarter in Latin - the rest in Romanian. He realised I was Romanian and took me out of the train, called an officer over to him, another Saxon from Transylvania ...

When I saw the line of carriages leaving without me, I knew I'd escaped. And so, instead of being sent west, with the others, to Germany, I was sent down to Romania. Alone! I had told the Saxons that there were other Romanians in the train, and they made a note of it, but ... they didn't do anything. Fine...! Since the Germans had behaved very correctly, with me, I said to myself, just wait till you get back home to your own Romanians... I wasn't expecting flowers and a fanfare at the station, but not far from it... At Cernauti station, the Germans handed me over to the Romanians. When I saw the Romanian uniform - even though it was of the gendarmerie - tears came into my eyes, I went over to them with my arms outstretched, ready to embrace them as if they were my own brothers. The gendarme officer swung at me and ordered me to stand to attention. They took me to their place, into an office, and the inquiry began: what had the Russians sent me for? Sabotage? Spying? Or both? I told them, and kept telling them what had happened and how - nothing! They put me in handcuffs. That's how they moved me to Baragan, in Slobozia, to Prisoner Camp No.1. As, of course, a prisoner and a Soviet...

"Two months of interrogation. I asked them to get information about me from my home village, where my mother, brother, cousins and uncles were; from Mana, where I'd been a teacher and where my wife and child were; from the teacher training college in Orhei, where I'd been a student, from the Inspectorate ... nothing. Because first, I had to tell them the t-r-u-t-h! And they were really sorry when the truth proved to be what I'd been saying from the very beginning, but not a word of ... apology didn't come into it, not even regret - nothing."

Father laughed nervously and went as white as a sheet. I knew that something even worse was to follow.

"If they hadn't beaten me... The pain doesn't matter, to hell with the pain, I'm not talking about the pain... Apart from ... the set-to in the school with the Tartar, and what followed - let's say I'd asked for it - not one Russian had ever laid a finger on me. I hadn't even been slapped on the face by one of them in uniform - we got sticks across the legs while we worked, from the guards, from the brigadiers, but not one NKVD-ist laid a hand on me..."

"There was no need to," I said.

"Well, yes, that's right. Isn't the work, the hunger and the cold enough to kill you? And anyway, those lot in uniforms considered us, the prisoners, as non-entities. Why should they tire themselves out with us? We wouldn't live anyway... But just look what happened in Romania, my Romania, my Romanians... And they called me 'Basarabian!' as if they were saying: 'Nobody!' or 'Spy!'

"In the camp, I was put in with the officers. They didn't beat any of the officers - but me, yes. Because I was... Basarabian. I told myself then that human stupidity knew no frontiers; it didn't matter what language you shouted or swore in. In fact, the Romanian's stupidity is even more..."

"I'm listening to you," I said. "So, the stupidity of the Romanian is..."

"As opposed to the Russian's stupidity - which is... like his country, endless; as opposed to the German's, swept into the corners, cubic, well-administered, you would almost think it was part of their machinery; our Romanian stupidity is... stupid, noisy, petty. The Romanian wants to make himself out as a peacock with beautiful feathers, haughty, and surprise surprise he's just a little sparrow, plucked and ridiculous... I told myself then that the stupidity of a nation is a kind of quality, a great people is a people capable of great, monumental imbecility, of historical stupidity - and since, as I see it, history is the twin sister of geography, I said to myself that great stupidity needs great space. It needs... vital space, hundreds of thousands of square kilo-metres, to express itself properly. So, the Romanian, even in his stupidity, remains petty, paltry, dulled by every square centimetre, a fool on his garden patch, an idiot in his courtyard..."

"I'm listening, I'm listening - and so, Romanian stupidity..."

"Right! That's enough of theories for now - I was just saying that, when they decided to get information and collect the evidence, my Romanian brothers were v-e-r-y disappointed: how was it possible, the suspect wasn't guilty?"

(One of the pieces of evidence which was collected - not by them but by us, by Mother and Grandmother - I have here with me, in exile: a photograph showing Father in Romanian military uniform, during one of the call-ups, before the 1940 surrender of Basarabia, that is. On the back, across the top of it, is Father's writing: *Chisinau, February 1940. E Goma*. Up the side, and on top of Father's writing is someone else's writing - a longer text: *This is to certify that we, the parish of the village of Mana, in the region of Orhei, confirm that the person photographed overleaf is none other than the teacher of the village of Mana, reg. Orhei, EUFIMIE GOMA, and we hereby sign and affix the parish seal to that effect. Parish priest. Gh. Dodon, 3rd March 1943*.)

"OK, then. Eventually, my Romanians let me go from the camp, after nine months - they needed the same period as a child, to ... not to take things in, the Romanians take things in quickly enough, as quick as lightening, but they didn't want to admit they'd taken the wrong things in... Anyway, there I was back home again... But His-to-ry, through her gendarme, was watching over me. OK, then! so I got rid of Grabenko as well in March '44, when we became refugees in Transylvania, where it was another story: while we were with the Germans, the Transylvanians considered us as refugees, deserters in a way, definitely invaders - hadn't we come to take the bread out of their mouths? After the 23rd August, when we weren't with the Germans any more, the Transylvanians started to consider us ... too anti-Russian - because they wanted Transylvania and who would give it to them? The Russians. However (and that's how life is, upside down) they called us bolsheviks, sent in advance to prepare the ground! The Romanian gendarmes considered us as ... well, the opposite: anti-Soviets. The proof: we'd fled from the Soviet regime. And to stop us fleeing any further, they hunted us down in the forests - with the precious help of the Romanian shepherd - and his flock - to hand us over to the Russians, to ... 'repatriate' us to Siberia.

"Well, in amongst all that bad fortune, there had to be some good fortune - even if a man had to make it for himself, with his own hands. And so the pair of us made our own fortune, in the camp at Sighisoara, in the spring of '45: you held the lantern for me, and goodness-gracious! I was able to give birth to your mother; and then to you - but somewhere else. And we were free from 'repatriation'! But not from suspicion. The authorities watched over us, took us in, asked us again whether we hadn't reconsidered (repatriation), and then we were defined as anti-Soviets, anti-Socialists - since we'd known Soviet socialism and we'd run away from it... The people around there still considered us pro-Soviets - while they, staunch anti-communists and anti-Soviets, joined the Communist Party and settled themselves into the new regime - but we were still the ones under suspicion; still refugees - who hadn't joined the Party! And we kept on telling them what had happened to us, in our past, but in their future...

"In '49, at Buia, in the first two days after that grenade had been thrown into their Party Headquarters at the school, your mother and I were suspected; but how come they didn't arrest us at the same time as the others, when they pulled the whole village in? Later, after they let us go (I was the last man to be freed and a long time after the man before me), we were still under suspicion: why had they kept us in for such a long time - 'they must be in with 'em...' You can never win - or as they say: you haven't got a hope in hell..."

191

I shrugged my shoulders. Nodded in agreement. I knew all about these things, I'd lived them to the full - I was already grown-up then.

"You'll see," Father continued, laughing, "that even if a miracle takes place and Romania is liberated from the Communists - and I said: liberated, that is, by someone else - we will still be suspected. Firstly, by the Basarabians who didn't become refugees in '44 : we did, so surely that means we deserted them, betrayed them? We should have stayed there and taken the rough with the smooth, as they did... Secondly, we'd be suspected by the non-Basarabians; on what grounds? Well: weren't the Basarabians 'repatriated' by the Russians? And why was that? I'll tell you why! - because they were in with them, they were agents of the Russians. Do you like it?"

No, I didn't like it.

Unfortunately - or fortunately - Father died in '67 and didn't experience ... the liberation of Romania; consequently he was spared from yet another opportunity of being under suspicion. Unfortunately, Romania didn't become liberated (and we're not talking of reflexives: doing it to oneself, but ... of the passive).

But the Romanians didn't need Romania to become liberated (passively) in order to look for, and even to find, suspects, guilty of their own bad fortune. However, they didn't look for guilty people among those standing right in front of them or those above them, who were keeping them on their knees, on all fours - they looked among the people at their side. These people were suspected (and therefore guilty) because, firstly, as Father said, they had realised much earlier than others the bad fortune which came from the East, and secondly, because they were downright dangerous.

How did they dare raise themselves onto two legs, and stand in the middle of the Baragan, full of indigenous Romanians who were down on all fours, and shout out that it was hurting them? What, did the cudgels and the

192

horsewhips only hurt *them*?

They hurt us all, but *we* didn't make a fuss about it - and anyway, we were Romanians, a rolling stone gathers no moss - we'd see what would be left of the mossy hillside in a few centuries, what would be left of them, the people who had beaten us and battered our brains: nothing. But us? Well, the Romanian had seven lives (in that steel heart of his) and however much the breakers tried to break him, he didn't move. That's how the Romanian survived.

Good Lies and Bad Lies

I was sitting on the *calidor*, waiting for today's families to leave.

They weren't relatives of ours, but of theirs, the ones who'd been taken away and hadn't come back. Today there were four women and a man: the mother and the wife of a man from one village, the wife and daughter of another man from another village; the man, who was the brother of another man from a third village, had brought them all here in his cart. To find out about their relatives who'd been pulled in.

I don't know who brought which gifts - but they'd brought: live hens and crabs, cakes and a piglet, a turkey and fish... And so Father was in the drawing room, telling them - who, what, how... I liked to think that this was what people had told Mother about him, before he came back from Balta two years ago, in all those telegrams and through the network. Only then, many more people used to come back. Now, from what I understood, only one had come back from the whole of Basarabia : Father.

And Father told them, he told them... What was he telling them about their relatives who'd been pulled in?

"I might have been young, but I still realised that you were lying to them," I said much later. "And not only were you lying to them, but you accepted their gifts as well - where were your principles: honour, truth...?"

"Don't worry, they were where they should have been," said Father. "It's true, you were too young, you couldn't understand. If you say you can remember, then you must remember that your mother was there all the time, while I was ... lying to them. She was there when I received the gifts as well. Didn't you ever wonder why...?"

"I did, I wondered about it, I asked her about it - she said she'd tell me when I was older."

"Well, now you are older, I'll tell you about it. You must have heard her talking in the house: when your mother was going here and there herself, to find out all she could about me from the people who'd come back, when *she* went bearing gifts... Do you know what they used to say to her?"

"That they hadn't seen you, that they hadn't even heard of you - that's why Mother used to cry."

"That wasn't all she was crying about. The few, very few, who had said that they didn't know anything about me - they just didn't know. Understandable, especially since I'd been pulled in at the beginning of January '41, while they were survivors of Balta - you've heard about what happened there..."

"Yes, thousands of people, who'd been pulled in after war was declared on 22nd June. Basarabians..."

"And after July first, 'suspects' from the left bank of the Dniester as well, I mean Russians and Ukrainians too... Some people talk of ten, others of fifteen thousand - only God knows the real figure, because the NKVD archives haven't got to Nuremberg yet... They didn't have the means to transport all those people from the front, they didn't want them to fall into Romanian hands - so they *liquidated* the camp: with machine guns, with grenades, with cannons, and anyone who tried to leave 'the zone', with flame-throwers... There's no doubt about it, the Germans learned a lot from studying statements of those who survived Balta, about liquidation... look, the Warsaw Ghetto - they could have learned a few things from Katjin as well..."

"Nevertheless, a lot of people got away..."

"It depends what you mean by a lot. One hundred survivors out of twelve thousand - not even one percent. The people who got away were mostly the first ones to be wounded or knocked out - other bodies fell on top of them ... After I'd come home I found out from an ... informant of your mother's, one who said that he'd seen me with his own eyes, not twenty feet from where he was standing, and that I'd been ripped in two by a bomb - because they used aircraft as well... The wretch, he shouldn't have come out of it alive!"

Father slammed his hand over his mouth:

"Lord no, I shouldn't have said that, he escaped and may the Lord be with him, and anyway, people only find out what really happened at Balta from him and others like him...

"As far as my fate was concerned... Sometime in January '44 I went into Orhei with your mother, and inside a shop your mother said: 'You see so-and-so, from such-and-such a village, he escaped from Balta and he told me he'd seen you lying dead on the ground next to him.' I asked her to go outside and wait for me, went over to the man, greeted him, calling him by name. He replied, but looked hard at me for a long time... 'Don't you recognise me?' I said. He looked at me, shook his head. 'No,' he said, 'I've got a good memory, when I've seen somebody once, I don't forget them.' 'That means you've never seen me before, then,' I said and took him by the arm and pulled him over to the shop window: 'Well, what about that woman on the pavement, have you seen her before?'

" 'Yes, I think so, she came to see us about three years ago, to ask me about her husband, a teacher in Mana...' 'And what did you tell her?' 'I can't remember.' 'I'll tell you what you told her: that her husband died at Balta, right next to you, ripped in two by a bomb!' 'I might have said that - but who are you anyway, questioning me like the police?' 'What, you don't recognise me, Old Iancu? I'm the dead man! I'm the poor sod who was ripped in two by the bomb!' He went white, then red. 'I hope the Ides are good for the Resurrection!' he said, trying to make a joke of it. 'It'll be your Resurrection next, you liar!' - and I grabbed him by the throat: 'Why did you lie to my wife, saying you'd seen me dead?' 'I didn't lie to her. I must have seen someone else with the same name as yours.' 'There isn't another teacher with my name, not in Mana, not in the Orhei region, not in the whole of Basarabia,' I said..."

"I hope you hit him."

"No, I didn't. And I'm sorry I didn't. And do you know what he said to me, the wretch? When I asked him: 'Why did you say you'd seen me dead when you didn't even know me when I was alive?' he said: 'The poor woman, she'd come all the way from Mana, on foot, with gifts - how could I let her go back with nothing? I had to say something.' 'And so you told her a lie - why couldn't you have made it a good one?' 'Yes, but if I told her a good lie, the lady would have wanted more details, many more - and then what would I have said? But you don't want details about a dead man - if he's dead, he's dead! That's the end of it!' Do you like it?"

"So that was why you decided to do the opposite?"

"I didn't have to wait to meet that idiot before I decided to do, as you say, the opposite. It's just human nature..."

"To lie? To tell ... necessary untruths? Necessary, but still lies!"

"A lie is bad only when it does someone harm."

"Interesting!" I laughed. "I can't remember you teaching your pupils that."

"You don't teach that kind of thing at school. A lie ... stops being untrue, when it's meant to keep people's spirits up, give them hope..."

"That's exactly the same theory that the Communists fall back on when they keep you hoping for a proletarian paradise."

"You can cut out comparisons like that! And there were the gifts as well."

"I'd forgotten! They paid you, so you had to give them something, even if it was only a lie."

Father became terribly annoyed. Not because I wouldn't believe him, but because I couldn't understand. At my age!

And hadn't I been in prison myself, in "obligatory residence"? He didn't say it, but that's what he must have been
thinking.

I withdrew, said that I'd only wanted to ... keep the
discussion going...

Sure, yes. He started again and said that he hadn't been
lying then. Because he hadn't said anything untrue to the
people who came to talk to him.

"They came to me, not to hear: yes or no, the man who
was pulled in is alive - because for them, he was alive in any
case; they came for confirmation: yes, it's possible - or nearly
certain - that their relative was living. Have you understood
now?"

"Yes, now I have. And I like it..."

"Like it or not, I'm speaking for myself now. If I'd
refused their gifts, from the very outset I'd have been giving
them an answer: no. Do you understand? When, like me,
you've escaped from what I'd escaped from; or like me, you
come back home from a place so far away and so ... deep
(you see, even now after twenty-odd years, I haven't even
told you two everything, in case you just thought I was
telling you a string of stories), there's no way you can crush
people's hope, in fact shouldn't you even help to keep it
intact? Anyway, my reckoning was quite simple: if I'd come
back from Arkhangelsk and from Uhta - after witnesses had
seen that I had died at Balta - why couldn't others come
back, people whom nobody had said had died? And so then,
where's the lie in that?"

Nowhere.

The Last Christmas

I was sitting on the *calidor*. And I wasn't trembling any more. Only my voice was trembling. I'd heard and I'd read that this was supposed to happen: "Carol singers with trembling voices", as the poem goes...

"Why do carol singers' voices tremble, Mother?"

"It's the emotion. And because of the cold," Mother said. "Christmas always falls in winter."

"Yes," I said, "but they're wearing lots of clothes, and they do say 'muffled up like a caroler'. Anyway, when you sing you warm yourself up, and fire comes out of you when you sing carols with passion - so why do their voices tremble?"

"With joy. Because Jesus was born."

"People don't tremble with joy. People tremble because of the cold, out of fear."

"Well out of fear, then," Mother said laughing. "Let's say: they're afraid of the dogs."

"Perhaps they're afraid, but not of the dogs," I said. "They're afraid of donkeys, of the donkey!"

That was it, that was definitely why: the carolers' voices trembled because they were afraid of the donkey. All our misfortunes were because of him - I'd seen him, with my own eyes, up on the common with the Gypsies who had been setting up their camp: he started to bray like the devil and kick and flick his ears like machine guns, and then he knocked one of the women over and then kicked her with his hooves, the blood was running like the river Raut, down beside her right eye and the baby in her arms stopped moving - I saw it all with my own, yes, all of it, and that was why I ran home and tore all the pictures of the donkey out

199

of the book: the one where Christ enters Jerusalem and the one at the front of the book, where the three men were following the star to find Him, with the frankincense and myrrh - I tore them all up, so that devil of an animal couldn't bray like the devil any more or kick with his hooves or flick his ears and whips and crowns of thorns, because he, the Donkey Devil had knocked nails in His hands and had, and had, and had k-i-l-l-e-d Him!

"What's wrong, why are you crying? Or are they just little icicles?"

I was tempted to tell Mother why I was crying, but if I had I wouldn't have had anything to cry about any more, she would have explained. She explained everything - that it wasn't Easter, when the nails were knocked in, it was only Christmas, when He was born, and that it wasn't possible, not even for Him, to die first and then be born - unless we changed the calendar like the Chinese had done. Or was it the Japanese, somebody like that.

"Come on, you go and sing with the others! Let's all go and sing carols," Mother said.

I wiped my tears away (melted icicles, nothing else) and followed Mother. Down into the courtyard.

But there were so many people there that even when I was sitting on someone's shoulders I could only see the top of the tree. I went back to my spot on the *calidor*. And sang there. I sang my carols from there.

I sang carols, trembling, my eyes glued to the fir tree which was as big as the school (and brought from far-far away, from the mountains), the fir tree which was decorated and sparkling with the balls and stars and burning with light from all the candles flickering in the wind, lighting up the courtyard as high as all the people could see, and burning away all the fires there had been until then: the Bonfire of the Books, the Bonfire of the Cross, the Bonfire of the Boys and Girls - burning. The tree said that now He'd been born, all our troubles were gone, we'd come back from our

Siberias and we were back together again with our families.

All the children had gathered around the tree in the schoolyard; and all the grown-ups who weren't children any more; and all the people who used to be children but had children of their own now - nearly all the people from the village. There were so many people that some of them had climbed up on the fence, others couldn't get in so stayed in the back lane, others sang from Old Iacob's courtyard, their voices were heard a little bit later, like the echo I'd learned from Father - for the songs with four voices.

That's what it was like. Because it was Christmas again. "Like before", the people said and I knew that it was not only the before I could remember, when I was a little-poor-orphan-mite, but even before that before; the very first before - that was why it was like the very first time. Because it was the first time Father had come back from Siberia; and the first time he'd put the tree up in the schoolyard; and the first time the grown-ups had come to the school tree; and the first time we'd all got into the sleighs, the long fur coats had a horrible smell of sheep, but the cold air smelled of falling over in the snow at night-time under the stars, the little horse bells sounded the same as the jingling bells on the stars we carol-singers-with-trembling-voices carried and the same as the sleigh bells in the manes of the winged horses who were flying over our heads; and it was the first time everybody, apart from the sleigh drivers, had sung carols for the nuns at Hirova; and the first time we'd all gone to Tabora, another nunnery and on the way back we sang lots of carols for the monks at Curchi. And I could hear, through the steamy mist with the sweet smell of incense and hot ovens, through the steamy mist with a gentle breeze of ice-cold air wafted behind by the sleighs - I could hear the voices of the grown-ups who were saying something about the nuns and the sisters, poor souls, that there were only about ten of them left up there, and about twenty down there because when we were occupied, the Russians had pulled them in, after they'd stripped them and shaved their heads; and it had been the same for the poor monks, all of them pulled in and sent to Siberia, not one had come back, like the nuns and sisters, shaved and stripped, poor souls, and I could hear how poor our rich monasteries had been left after the Russians had robbed them and left them in ruins, three years ago - and I also heard: "But if we wait, little by little..."

Old Iacob had stayed at home, he was the mayor and always on duty watching over the village. The next day he asked me what the carol singing at the monasteries had been like. I told him what I'd heard:

"The poor monasteries, what poor, wretched monasteries, Old Iacob. And the poor nuns, poor souls, and the poor monks - because the Russians, you know what they did" - and I added: "But if we wait, little by little..."

"That's right, my littl' lad!" Old Iacob said. "Littl' by littl'..." and then he said: "I'm sorry now I didn't come to th' carol singin', up at th' monasteries. Shame you didn't take th' old woman wi' you, up t' th' monasteries t' sing a farewell carol."

"What do you mean farewell, Old Iacob? Are you thinking about leaving Mana? Where are you going?"

"We're not thinkin' about goin' anywhere, but th' times 're thinkin' about havin' somethin' happen to us, 'cause it's not what man wants, it's what God gives," said Old Iacob. "An' just look, Headmaster-sir's or-gan-ised a Christmas tree, an' a Christmas an' carol singin', as if it was th' Last Supper..."

"Shut up, Iacob, stop your croakin' an' forebodin'!" said Aunt Domnica. "What's got into you, talkin' like that to a littl' kid?"

"Well, somethin's got into me. An' he should remember, this littl' lad o' mine, when 'e grows up..."

"What should I remember, Old Iacob?"

"This 'ere Christmas," Old Iacob said and pointed to the

floor. " 'Cause we'll not see another one..."

"Shut up, Iacob, you prophet o' doom! You'd think you were on yer death bed - an' this littl' kid hasn't got a clue what you're talkin' about..."

At the time, no, this little kid didn't have much of a clue about it. No clue at all, in fact. Not even by the next Christmas, in '44, spent in the forest at Buia, afraid of "repatriation"; nor by the Christmas of '45, spent in a village school office, far-far away, far away from the Christmas which seemed to have always just begun and never ended, in the schoolyard at Mana - where nearly all the villagers had gathered around the Christmas tree, when after the pupils had finished singing a carol they'd been taught by Mother and Father (in two, three and even four voices), one of the parents would start singing another one; and all the people of his age would join in and, in unison, tell us the story of what had happened to the unicorn with the stars on his horn, and how they, the hunters, hadn't shot him with their arrows - out of pity and astonishment; and then the pupils started again, in four voices, with their little round pretzel mouths and eyes fixed on Father's hand which was beating time very assuredly, and on the signs for when to come in, which the parents didn't understand; and after that the women started singing stories, their voices cutting through the thick woollen shawls, about the young bride who says farewell to her brothers and mother, to her brothers and sisters, to the garden full of flowers; and then the children started again; and after them the young men sang carols, telling us about the fir trees and the sycamores; and once again - in came the teachers and the pupils in four voices, to add a little bit of Christianity to the Orthodox pagan-ity of the Manians. Old Iacob was very right in what he said, none of which I understood at the time, but later, much later in fact, my parents explained it to me:

The Manians had their own "pagan" mixed-up carols, a line or at most a verse thrown in here and there which mentioned Jesus being born, but for the rest, they reverted to the unicorns and the fir trees and the weddings with the stars. As for carol singing, they went around caroling in large groups, going from one house to the next, to their friends and to their enemies - Christmas was the time when people made up, they "forgave" one another, some said simply, "Forgive 'im", and crossed themselves; other people with grudges said, "So-and-so's forgiven", and would call out to him by name and touch him on the shoulder. After all that was finished, their purpose changed - first they knocked on the gates with their sticks, which meant that their host had to tie up the dogs (which, at Christmas, were all supposed to be tied up behind the house), then they trampled noisily through the courtyard, stomped up the steps which lead to the open gallery (or porch or verandah, it depended...), after that they trampled up and down on the gallery, whispering and humming in echoes and trying to find a space under a window - and, in the end, they asked:

"Are you receivin' carolers?"

They didn't wait for an answer from the house, because the question was the first line of the carol - and they sang the rest of the carol under the window (if there was one). After which the host opened the door wide:

"Come in! Come in with the Tidings!"

And they went in with the Tidings, and gave the Tidings once again inside the house - and the Tidings they gave spoke of bards and unicorns and archers, and Glad Tidings about the Child.

For the Manians, the school Christmas tree was an official school festival, introduced by the "Romanians", and so they went there (if they did go) usually only to escape a fine, but the singing in one-two-three-four voices, with all kinds and times of "coming in", "choruses" and the rest was, for them a ... joke - like school, a place you had to go to, to learn lots of things which would be of no use to you in life and didn't even come from these here parts. But that

Christmas, in '43, everybody had come, had come to the school, to the tree. Perhaps they were feeling what Old Iacob had felt - and Aunt Domnica was afraid of...

"...that they wouldn't be singing carols any more, neither under the windows nor at the school tree; not even their 'pagan' carols - but Lord, they were so lovely, so lovely..." Mother said later, much later.

"Something like that," said Father. "They sensed disaster was coming. They sensed it was their last Christmas. It might have been ours as well, our last Christmas, if we hadn't left..."

"If they sensed it was going to be the last time, why didn't they leave as well?" I asked.

"They would have sensed it in the form of: 'I'm afraid that...'," said Father. "When you say that you know something, it means you're completely certain about it; when you say you sense something, this sensation can be either good or bad; but if you say, as the Basarabian does: 'I'm afraid that...', you are afraid, not of what's going to happen to you, but of the fact that you can't do anything about it."

"It's more than that," said Mother. "When a Basarabian says that he's afraid, *I'm afraid the cart's broken down on the road*, you can be *sure* that the cart is already broken... How can you do anything about something which is already happening or has already happened to you?"

"You can run away," said Father. "Like we are now (we were in the forests in Transylvania). Taking to his healthy heels, isn't that the Romanian's weapon?"

"It might have made our heels healthy, but as a weapon it hasn't protected the general health all that well," Mother said.

"You can joke about it now," Father smiled, "but just as well you didn't say things like that then, in '44..."

(The conversation took place every year, and the "then" soon became the "thens": '45, '46, '47, '48, '49, '50...

("Hang on until I get my breath back," one of us said,

" '51, '52..."

("Mind you don't count into the future as well!" another one of us laughed. " '53, '54, '56..."

("But aren't we the same people as we were in '40 under the Occupation, now in the golden era of mankind? '58, '59, '60...")

"I was always thinking of the boy," Mother picked up again. "If it hadn't been for the child, I wouldn't have left my house, with a knapsack on the end of a stick over my shoulder, to go among strangers..."

"Sure, sure! And you would have woken up without your knapsack and without your stick, on the banks of the Aral entertaining your brother - but if you'd had a bit more nouse, you'd have ended up on the coast of the USSR's Magnific-Pacific, and there you would have seen some real Christmases, with the same carols as were sung in the time of Prince Stephen the Great and Holy - if not even from the times of Prince Christmas himself..."

"I don't know what you're laughing about: the further our people are from their homes, the more they uphold their traditions, preserve their language - look at the example of the Romanian language and Latin. Then there was no talk of...'a specific national character' - what specific character: *Maldavyian* *? You've heard on Radio Chisinau what kind of language they've imposed; a language that doesn't exist! While over there, miles away, in the far east..."

"I get the jist, but you're just quoting from your friend, Ludmila Greenhouse!" Father laughed.

"I'm not quoting, and she's called Tamara anyway; and not Greenhouse, but Whitehouse..."

"White or green, they're still walls aren't they..."

"I'm not quoting from my friend Tamara, I'm quoting from our enemy, the *Linguistic Atlas of the USSR* ! "

"To quote from something, you've got to be able to read

---

*Moldavian, a parody of Russian pronunciation.

it first - and you don't speak Russian."

"I know the letters, enough to be able to work out the name of a village on the banks of the Amur."

"Not Chistelnita by any chance?" Father laughed.

"If I had a more detailed map, perhaps I'd find Chistelnita as well, nigh on fifty families were deported from around our way, and over a hundred people without families, bachelors that is - if they'd all been taken to the same place they would have made up two villages..."

"And that's only speaking of around your way... Our Basarabians, poor souls, is there anywhere they haven't been scattered..."

"You can tell where they've been, their Atlas says: Indaratnici, Scorteni, Lunga - and you notice, I'm only giving you the names which haven't got Slav endings. And Inul, Aur, Dunarea - those are near Habarovsk, on the Amur. And: Orheii-Noi, Floresti, Calarasi - and where on earth do those names come from, if not from our own deported Basarabians? According to their linguistic Atlas, there are about 3,000 Romanian speakers on the Pacific coast - and you have to take into account the fact that they lie about statistics, in general, and about linguistic statistics in particular. Only God knows how many thousands and thousands haven't been entered as having Romanian as their mother tongue in the census figures..."

"I thought we'd been talking about something else before - what were we talking about?"

"About everything and nothing: about the last Christmas for the Basarabians in Basarabia, in '43," said Mother.

The Name

The *calidor* of the house in Mana faced north. Just by chance really, if that teacher father of mine had found another piece of land for the school somewhere else, it would have faced in another direction - but at any rate, it would have faced the back lane.

The *calidor* of the house in Mana, despite facing directly north, wasn't exposed to the icy north wind - which in Mana blew from the north-east. The longest and biggest of the school buildings, which was constructed square in front of the house, protected it - and not only from the wind. It protected the *calidor* as much as it could. That is, it didn't.

The *calidor* of the house in Mana was the hub of the universe. The paths for running away, the roads for trekking, the corridors for moving flocks, the boulevards for incoming invasions - they all passed through there - all of them intersecting one another for the sake of good business. The threshold of my birth (equidistant between the 46th and the 48th parallels - but not exactly on the 47th parallel - and roughly on the 29th meridian) was such a compelling location that a writer, who at first wandered from one style to another and was mediocre, and who later became a "realist-socialist" and downright terrible, called it with good reason (and this time it so happened that he didn't make a mistake): "The Gate of Unrest".

And through this Gate, at a trot or at a gallop - but always from east to west - rode all the people from the deserts and the marshes: Ostrogoths, Visigoths and pure Goths, Huns and Avars, Slavs and Bulgarians, Magyars and Petchenegs and Cumans, Tartars and Cossacks. And Russians. And Soviets.

My birthplace witnessed over nearly two thousand years (I say "nearly" because I'm taking the end as the 21st June 1941*) only one movement in the opposite direction: that of the peace-loving and eternally transient Carpathian shepherds, looking for new pastures on the northern coast of the Black Sea, from Azov on the Caspian Sea.

It would appear that I owe my name to these people swimming-against-the-current.

"Why are we called Goma, Father? The children laugh at me: 'Guma, Gum, Chewing Gum, Rubber, Gomos, Goma *sifilitica*, Gummy Face...' Even some of the teachers make fun of my name - couldn't you find a proper one?"

Father shrugged his shoulders and laughed:

"Names aren't there for the finding. They're like a cross or a wife: you have them, you wear them - you bear them..."

"But when you were in the camp at Sighisoara, when the Russians wanted to ... repatriate-us-to-their-country, and you made those false papers and 'made us be born', Mother and I, somewhere else - you could have changed our names as well. Others did..."

"I don't know of one Basarabian who changed his name. I've only heard of people who re-Romanianized their names after they'd been made to sound more Russian in the days of the tsars. Perhaps if I'd tried to change it ... I would have succeeded, I was the one holding the pen after all... But I didn't want to. When you get married, you'll see that your name's like your wife: in time, you pick something up from it and it from you, and each of you gives something to the other one, and you model yourselves on each other..."

Some time later, quite a while later :

"Why are we called what we are, Father? I wonder what the first one of us was called?"

At first Father laughed, then he assumed the air of a real, old-fashioned teacher:

*June 1941 - 22 June 1941 was the beginning of German aggression against the Soviet Union.

"Well if we stopped to think about it carefully, then we'd have to arrive at the conclusion that the first one was called Adam - because the second one must have been called Gomorrah..."

"Hmm, yes... It's an old name."

"And like all those names, it's easy to pronounce."

"Hmm, yes - let's see: Nebuchadnezzar..."

"In any case, despite some variations in spelling and pronunciation, our name is to be found in Iran, in Egypt, in black Africa - around Lake Tanganyika there are tribes of them: Ugoma, Kigoma, Ngoma (or N'Goma), there's even an area beside Lake Kivu called by our name..."

"I wonder what it means in ... Tanganyikan? If not even in Gomaian!"

"As the Basarabian says: I'm not telling you..." laughed Father. "I'm not telling you," he continued, "because I don't know - how on earth should I know?"

"Let's forget about the name, for the time being - what about our bloodline, where does that come from?"

"I'm not telling you - all right, I'll tell you: from the heart!" Father was still laughing. "How should I know? We haven't got any papers, before my father they were all illiterate."

"Illiterate from generation to generation, or did they become illiterate?" I asked him. "I'm thinking of those Armenians who settled in Basarabia, in the villages, and who forgot how to read and write in their own language, or the Jews in Maramures - again they'd settled in the villages and become farmers..."

"I don't think we've got any Armenian or Jewish blood - although you can never be sure, can you?" Father replied. "That's what I think, judging by the name: it doesn't look as though it originates from them - in any case, in the village they used to call my grandfather, my father's father, *The Aromanian*."

"I know. *The Macedonian*, that is." *

* Also means *the mosquito*.

210

"Yes, but don't forget, there are Macedonians and Macedonians: there are the ones the Bulgarians and the Yugoslavs quarrel over, who speak a Slav language which *they* say is called Macedonian - what on earth have the Slavs who ended up there after the sixth century A.D. got to do with the Macedonians, who had a kingdom, later an empire, more than a thousand years earlier? It's a Slav language, Cyril and Methodius based their work on it, when they invented (how else can I put it?) Slavonic..."

"Grandfather - your father - is called Cyril..."

"So what? It's a Greek name, it means lord, and it has come down to us through the Christian calendar, not through... I read somewhere that the Bulgarians and the Greeks are still arguing about Cyril and Methodius: the Bulgarians say that the pair of them were Bulgarian through and through, otherwise how could they have known the language? The Greeks say they were of pure Greek blood, from Salonika..."

"And what do you say, Dad? You've got to have some theory or other."

"Not a theory, exactly, but I read somewhere that Cyril and Methodius were pure Vlachs, from Pella - that is, Macedonians, Armenians - hence the conclusion that we poor people taught the Slavs how to read and write, made Christians of them..."

"Hey... and just look how many poor Slav souls were made into Christians!" I laughed. "But getting back to the Aromanians: they came much more recently, in the last hundred years, after the Greeks won their independence and started cutting their Jews back: the Macedonians and the Albanians - perhaps we're descended from the survivors of the cut-backs?"

"I don't know. I don't think so - if that had been the case, we would have kept up contact with 'the tribes' who settled at Predeal and Lugoj. I looked into it: I couldn't find any link. We're either a dying race - because there's nobody else with our name in Basarabia, not even in Moldavia - or we came here a long time ago, a long, long time ago..."

"How long ago?" I asked, laughing. "What, in 335 B.C. with Alexander the Great?"

"If I'm not mistaken, it was a little bit earlier than that, in the reign of King Philip II, his father," Father laughed seriously. "If not even earlier, when Darius crossed the Danube into Basarabia at Isaccea before conquering the Macedonians, and why not, perhaps in amongst the chariot drivers there was someone of our name who looked after the donkeys..."

"Hmm, yes... it's not a bad idea," I said.

"And if that's so, let's telephone the Shah, ask him to look through his archives - imagine if we found out we were Persians!"

"Better not phone him, who knows what else we might find out and we'd spoil our little game - what the hell, anyway, aren't we Daco-Romans? Through and through? Pure blood, the lot? Of course we are!"

"It wouldn't spoil anything for me," said Father. "But let's hope Trajan and Decebal don't get annoyed about it..."

"...Decebal...off-his-horse-and-make-him-fall..."

"...But I really don't feel as though I'm... the fruit of love of either of those two characters. My Daco-Roman blood comes from that Aromanian father of mine, and from my mother, a Polack - I led them all a dance, getting married to your mother, a genuine, true-born little Romanian, a Popescu..." *

"According to you, Father, a Popescu, but according to Mother, a Greek - and just what kind of Greek..."

"You can well imagine that I know what kind of Greek she is, but the blood isn't important, it's the name that counts, and it's the only -*escu* in the family..."

"Well, what if we climb back down the Popescu family

---

* *Popescu* - the most common Romanian surname.

212

tree, right back to the first Popescu, and find out that His Holiness was Serbian? Or had a bit of Bulgarian in him? Or a tiny bit of Russian - *slava Bogu*, their name is legion: Popov, Popovici, Popoff, Popenko - there might even be a Popowski, but the ending sounds Polish to me; are the Poles Orthodox as well?"

"Three or four of them, three Belorussians and a Ukrainian. And half a Russian..."

"Is there any point in going on? I mean, where do we look next?"

"No, not really. It's better that we don't know - if you don't know, you can pretend it's just a straight line right back to the beginning..."

"...right back to our ancestors the Vth Legion... You see, we end up back at our poor Macedonians after all..."

"Hmmhmm," Father said. "Or, as the people of Bucharest say: the Macedonians who were *cursed*, who came from Palestine..."

Father said - another time:

"Whatever our name is or comes from, it impressed the Russians. The last one to remark upon it in the prison administration asked what kind of a name's that? At the beginning I said it was Romanian. The man gave me a dirty look: 'What are you lying for? It's Italian!' and, proud of his own knowledge, he changed it on his documents and then made me out new papers - with double *m*..."

"And was it any use to you, the Italian name?"

"Well, it didn't just stop at him - they're strange, the Russians: where I was, I was meeting up with all kinds of 'national representatives', but *they* didn't seem quite so impressed. They only asked... whether they'd noted it down correctly - in their alphabet and according to its derivation... They were quite used to Romanian names, but they challenged you to make the choice: 'Romanian or Moldavian?' as if they weren't the same thing anyway... After a time - especially as some people were pronouncing it *Homa*, I started saying that I was Romanian ... of Latin origins - and added that my name was derived from the Latin *homo* which means *man* - and to really floor them, I rattled out: '*Homo-homini-lupus*! *Ecce homo*!' "

"Were they as impressed by the Latin as the Germans were?"

"Now you're talking! But most of all the Russians were bowled over by the fact that somebody was called Man, Homo... 'One of 'em's called *Celoviek* - he's Latin!' Can you believe it? At one stage, a German tried to get in on the act: 'My name, Mann, means *celoviek* as well.' 'In what language?' the Russian asked him. 'In German.' 'It might mean that in German, but it doesn't in Latin!' That Russian put him in his place. He-he! The Latin name saved me from a lot of things. You could even say that it saved my life."

"How's that?"

"It's simple: the pen-pushers in the camps, impressed by my name, talked to me for just that little bit more; and during the chat, they found that I was a ... *profiesor* (I wasn't the only one ... teacher, that is, but the others didn't have Latin names), and they asked me if I could ... read and write! Well, somehow I'd started to get by in Russian ... speaking it, but writing it ... I was hopeless. Luckily, however, they didn't take me right out of the work gangs to put me somewhere where I had to write: in the service sections you didn't need a teaching qualification - in the latrines, that is; nor in the kitchens - I don't mean the actual kitchens (not even 'Latins' had access there), just carrying the food on your back - but that kind of work meant life, not death.

"I made the most of these 'jobs', learned to write in Russian and at the first opportunity, I was promoted: I became a surgeon's assistant! Mind you, I did pass the examination ... in Latin. I was examined by one of their officers, who said he was a doctor, and I just rattled out: '*Radius - cubitus - calcareous - astragalus*...', all I could remember of anatomy.

"And so, instead of continuing to dig the canals, to cut down the forests, to unload the English armaments, I became a surgeon's assistant. As in the kitchens, I wasn't involved in real medicine, but was just affiliated to it: I was a cleaner, my job was to look after the bed-pans at night... You see, that's why I didn't want to change my name, from the moment I'd been 'repatriated'..."

"There's nothing Latin about it at all," I put in, "but it definitely sounds like other Aromanian names, Armenian ones, Macedo-slav ones: Goga, Goja, Gose, Joja, Boga, Loga..."

"Aromanian maybe, but pastoral more like," said Father. "It would appear that we didn't come over on horseback, but behind a flock of sheep, and not with lances - but with crooks... The sheep trail..."

"But the sheep trail didn't pass through the Orhei region. It was further south, in the Bugeac."

"There's no law to say so. They passed through here as well, after they'd been further north, around Soroca. After that they followed the river Bug and the Nipru down to the sea..."

"How do you know?"

"I don't. I'm guessing. Otherwise what would a single Aromanian be doing in a village in the heart of a forest? He could only be there if he was a shepherd, moving his sheep through... And he stayed there... to become one of the flock. Perhaps he fell in love with one of the local girls, or he might have fallen ill and been left there by the others to be looked after, but they didn't stop to pick him up on the way back..."

"Or they might have come to pick him up, but in the meantime the invalid had got to grips with the landlady's daughter and he had five children or more."

"Anything's possible. Especially since we haven't any papers. Don't you think it's better like that? When you don't know where you come from and whose father you are, as the Wallachians say, you can pretend what you like. Because you've got no papers..."

"And what about Mother? What's the score there?"

"Talk to her about it. But you'll do the talking; she'll just sit and say nothing. Hers is a different story."

The Un-Nameable

I didn't ask Mother about it, for the very reason that I knew she'd say nothing. I knew there were reasons for her silence... political ones, if nothing else. Besides, since she had never broached the subject herself...

Much later on - Father had died by then - I visited her in the hospital, a book under my arm:

"I'll read you a passage from the biography of..."

On hearing the name, Mother's face lit up. But only for a second. She immediately reverted to the suspicious, hostile look I'd come to know since she'd been ill.

She asked me a barrage of questions which came at me like machine-gun fire (as Father would have said), questions which bore no relation to the book, as if to fend off my bringing up the topic. Nevertheless, I tried to make my way through - not the questions, which had foregone conclusions anyway - but the "information" in Giurescu,* according to which a poor cousin, who'd been brought over from Greece and charged with the administration of the estates in Balti and Orhei, had...

Although she was listening to me, Mother was pretending to be interested in much more important things - for example, when on earth was I going to finish university and eventually get a degree, and therefore, status - but I could forget about work until I was at least thirty-five...

"Enough of my age and my degree status! We're supposed to be talking about..."

"Sssh!" Mother interrupted, with her finger over her lips.

---

*Constantin C. and Dinu Giurescu, prolific authors of official academic works on aspects of Romanian history, including *History of the Romanians*.

"Somebody might hear..." - and she pleaded with me with her eyes, her eyes were all she had left.

"Who's going to hear us? The woman in the next bed, Princess ... Fanariotidi?"

"Sssh! That's not her name, her name's... But it doesn't matter what her name is. Look, if you like, we can have a little chat, as long as we don't mention any surnames - what do names matter anyway? That's about right, what you say's written there. My grandfather, my mother's father, was called Iacob... you-know-what, we mustn't mention his surname... One of mother's brothers was called Gheorghe ... same surname ... but we mustn't say it out loud. This Gheorghe was Ion's father, Ion ... you-know-what, my cousin, the one you argued with."

"Hang on a minute! This Gheorghe ... I-know-what, the father of Ion let's-not-mention-his-name, can't be one and the same with cousin Gheorghe from Greece."

"Poor cousin," Mother specified, winking at me, raising her finger and repeating - " *the* poor cousin!"

"The cousin who was poor, over there in Greece, but as soon as he got his hands on the estates of..."

"Sssh! I did ask you: no surnames. Not Gheorghe, Ion's father, but Gheorghe, his great-grandfather, he's the Gheorghe, you-know-who's cousin ... but no names..."

"How could I not know who? So, only the two of us know that you're a distant relation of ... we-both-know-who. Why don't you want to say his name ... the man who remains nameless?"

"What's the point?" Mother was astonished. "I'd say it, but he doesn't need me to, I mean, he doesn't need me to say his name out loud, for him to be what he is - and anyway, the name might just suit him, after all, a dog's not the only thing with a docked tail!"

"You can't get out of it now, you've recognised him!"

"All right, I've admitted it. You're carrying on like the interrogators at Medias when we were brought up from the kitchens!" Mother laughed, then she panicked, and then laughed at her own panic. "It's not a good idea for them to find out..."

"Who's going to find out, and what? You mean, since the Communists took over, you've been frightened to 'black-mark' your dossier with his name..."

"Where did you get that from, *frightened*? I've never been afraid of anything! And if you really want to know, I've never even thought about it, about him. Come to think about it, I'm not afraid to say his name...you-know-whose. I'm ashamed..."

"You're ashamed that you're descended from Prin..."

"Sssh! Haven't I told you not to mention his name? And I'm not descended from any prince...like I've told you, from a cousin of his, and a poor cousin at that."

"So that's what bothers you: that this ancestor of yours was poor! But he didn't stay like that for long: as soon as he set foot in Basarabia..."

"Poor, rich - it doesn't matter! Well, it does matter, but the other way round: My mother broke off relations with her family of, of, of...of sharp-nosed fat Greeks, of, of of... You know, the things which have been written about the Greek lease-holding farmers aren't lies! They really were outright *parvenus* - but they weren't old, they were new!" Mother laughed, pleased with her allusion to Filimon's novel.

"But this Gheorghe we-know-who wasn't just any lease-holding farmer; he was the cousin of... He was cousin and administrator."

"He could have been his brother, as far as his nature was concerned; a *parvenu*, I can tell you. He still had the soul of a lease-holding farmer even after he became lord and master. I don't know what it says in that book you've brought with you, but I do know that Gheorghe, the first one, just followed his sharp-nosed instinct and got his hands on his cousin's estates - as master of them... But to hell with them, what are we wasting our time talking about the Greeks for?

My name's Popescu and that's the end of it!"

"Why does that have to be the end of it? Are you ashamed? Ashamed that Grandmother ran away from her father's house with a poor boy - who was called Popescu besides, and nicknamed Holban?"

Mother frowned. Then immediately relaxed again. She nodded in agreement. Slowly. It might have been in sad agreement. But it wasn't. In Mother's eyes a spark was flickering - of pride, I'd say, but in any case, of pleasure.

"She did the right thing!" she said. "And she did the right thing to that Greek, the old thief - I'm talking about Iacob...you-know-what. Do you know what he wanted to do? To sell his daughter off to the richest man he could find, and by force..."

"What...was he a *parvenu* as well? Another Greek?"

"Yes, he was a kind of *parvenu* as well, but he wasn't a Greek; he was a wop."

"You mean Italian."

"Sort of. Iacob, the big Greek..."

"Why do you say that? Was he tall? Heavily built?"

"I never laid eyes on him in my life - that would have been the final straw! The only time I ever went over to where they were, to their village, was in the holidays for a ball - I was at teacher training college...and along came, not a child but a...snivel of a kid, and stood in front of me, a young lady... It was that little Greek cousin of mine, Ion, who without any ceremony whatsoever, invited me to their place, to the Court... When I heard him say Court...I told him...I can't remember what excuse I gave him for not going, and then the little snot said something awful to me - I can't remember what..."

"Something to do with poverty?"

"What else could one of them, that family of Greeks, think of saying? Well, when I slapped him across the face, I knocked him on the floor! I was strong. I'd been working in the fields, taking turns reaping with Father and my brother

220

Niculae... And of course, I'd been insulted..."

So, Mother had been insulted... And where? Right in the middle of the dance! She swept away the insult with a slap across the face - which knocked the little Greek snot of a cousin of hers to the floor; but she had to leave, run away, because the cousin had informed on her and The Boys moved in... Where have I heard all that before?

"Luckily I was already with your father, we ran away on the bicycle - but not to my family at Chistelnita, but to Ciocalteni, where your father rallied his family together - as soon as those Macedonians heard they had the chance to get their teeth into raw Greeks..."

"So the horsebound expedition - your mother's pursuers - went to Chistelnita, then?"

"That's right! They broke down the little gate, pulled down a fence, cut down the cherry tree in the courtyard - it was one of those that gave white cherries, as big as this, look... They're barbarians, the Greeks... Only Father was at home, Mother was up on the hillside at the vineyard, otherwise they'd... And they spread manure over our gallery, that was what annoyed us the most..."

"You mean: the horses did."

"Who's going to get a horse up on a gallery? But don't worry, we showed them two or three nights later."

"You mean with Dad's Aromanians?"

"I mean me and my mother. We didn't need any Aromanians to help us set a light to things, did we? We burned all their wheat - unfortunately it was spread over quite a wide area..."

"You burned the wheat? Didn't you feel bad about it, if only for the devastation?"

"Do you think that old thief broke his heart over our cherry tree? And over the gate?"

"Didn't you get into trouble with the gendarmes?"

"The gendarmes! They were used to family quarrels and didn't get involved. They knew the Greeks took the law into

221

their own hands - their own law! Afterwards, that little Greek cousin of mine wanted to set fire to something himself and so he went up to our windmill - only he came across my mother who'd made a little shelter up there and was on the lookout - didn't Ion tell you what happened?"

"He didn't, I found out something from that girl cousin of mine, though. Something about a ... hot pepper? Wasn't that just a story the Basarabians put around?"

"What a story! Ten of the neighbouring villages were splitting their sides laughing about it for years - why do you think he got stuck with the name: Capsicum...?"

"Did Grandmother really do it? Did she really shove a pepper up his...?"

"Right up," Mother giggled. "But she made sure to cut it open first, and hone it down, nice and long..."

"And you wonder why he hasn't come to visit you once in the hospital, over these five years..."

"Just let him show his face here..."

Only in the second or third year of "obligatory residence" in Baragan did I find out that I had an uncle on Mother's side of the family. A second cousin, really, he was Mother's cousin... Father broke the important news to me, but was quite clear about the fact that I shouldn't mention him in front of Mother.

Because their first meeting - after thirty years - had passed from a hello to a heated argument in seconds - with Ion's second wife and the two children on one side, and Father supporting Mother on the other. They were arguing about hectares, and about being slapped on the face (but not, however, about being knocked to the floor), and then about three other hectares, vineyards, windmills...

God knows how long the quarrel would have gone on if Mother hadn't cut it short by saying just one word: "Capsicum!" At the sound of the word, my uncle's eyes grew as big as saucers and he suggested that my father should just take half of it and leave, otherwise he couldn't be held responsible for what happened. Which Father did, there and then...

During another visit to the hospital, I asked her:

"What happened when your parents ran away from the Court?"

"Court? Gypsy-king! He was just a wandering *parvenu* swept in with the tide!"

"Well, when they ran away from home, then. What happened?"

"What could have happened? It was just like any other time - nearly half the women married were girls who had run away."

"So it wasn't a Greek custom."

"What do I know about Greek customs! My name's Popescu - if you didn't already know! And that's the end of it! I don't know how Toader Popescu, Holban's son, got together with the daughter of... you-know-who, but in any case, they agreed to run away."

"So, Grandfather didn't actually steal Grandmother away."

"But I've told you before: the girl, the bride - is stolen away when...she's stolen, that is, from the wedding, during the actual ceremony - but before the priest has pronounced them man and wife. That's what it means when a girl's stolen away. But if the bride-to-be leaves *before* the wedding - a day, or a week before - then that means she's only run away. They even decide on the time and place, often they have accomplices..."

"Did Grandmother have people who were in on it?"

"She must have. Otherwise she wouldn't have been able to escape from..." She was about to say: prison.

"So, on the chosen night, when the moon was hidden behind a cloud, Toader came up to the stile and started cuckoo-ing like a cuckoo!" I laughed.

"It was a bit more complicated than that, the old thief

223

sensed that she was going to try something - but she still managed to get away!"

"On horseback?"

"How else but on horseback?" Mother's face beamed. "A horse, around our way... He-he! The horse was certainly your better half..."

"Whose, yours? And the girls? Did you ride? Side-saddle, like the Amazons?"

"I don't know where on earth you got that idea, that the Amazons rode side-saddle. When you say on horseback, you really mean: on horse-back!"

"Did you wear jodhpurs?"

"Jodhpurs? What would I want with them? Do you think the trousers make the horseman? No, my dear, the horse makes the horseman."

It sounded nice: the horse made the horseman - but hadn't she said it just a little bit too nicely? For years, for so many years, Mother had been confined to bed. Mainly because of her legs. Her pins which used to be so nimble. Now they were dead, twisted, deformed and shrunken. Perhaps that's why I always remembered her dancing - always dancing. And perhaps that's also why I remembered the horse - even though I couldn't remember her riding... But perhaps I could? No, what I could remember was...the horses in Mana, the games on the common - but that was just children playing, little boys having a grand time... No, that's not right, because the girls joined in as well - and, of course, that ugly, sickly one, one of Scridon's daughters - she couldn't walk, but when she was on a horse... People in the village used to say that if Scridon's daughter wanted to get married, she'd have to stay up on the horse - because when she dismounted, she was so ugly ... her hips didn't work...

"How did you ride?" I asked her.

"Well, on horseback!" Mother laughed. "Without a saddle, no bridle, no stirrups - what did God give horses manes for, and why did he give me two legs? Two legs..." She repeated in a lower, slower voice.

"Did Grandmother ride as well?" I said, changing the subject.

"Ho! Even after she got married, but only outside the village."

"But Grandfather didn't have any horses."

"When they ran away, he didn't. My parents ran off with little cousin Mihai's horses - that's where they hid out anyway for the first week. After they'd been married - by the priest - they settled into their own house, Father's, I mean. That's where they were met by the 'expedition' organised by that old thief - the second 'expedition', that is. He was there with two of his sons, Mother's brothers, with servants, cowherds - all of them on horseback... Father was quite...shy, he went into hiding..."

"What do you mean, he went into hiding? He was the one who'd stolen the girl? He should have..."

"Have what? Firstly, Father didn't go into hiding because he was afraid - he was a mild, gentle-natured man, but he wasn't scared of anything. He simply didn't want to have to face the Greek empty-handed, not for his sake, but for Mother's... He wanted to avoid... Anyway, secondly - and this is what the villagers said - Father hadn't stolen Mother away; it was the other way round..."

"The other way round! But surely Grandfather did the stealing!"

"I don't think 'stealing' came into it!" Mother laughed. "It must have been something like this - Mother said to Father, 'Toader! Do this, here, then!' Father: 'Hang on a little bit, let's think about it, give it some consideration...' Mother: 'I'm not going to hang on, and we're not going to think about it. Do what you're told, otherwise...' "

"Otherwise what?"

"Well, people exaggerate you know, especially in the country, but there must have been some truth in it..."

"In what, that she used to hit him?"

"No! That's just what people said because of the staff."

"Did she beat him with a staff?"

"No! That's what people said, but really she just pretended to..." - and Mother smiled.

"They made up a legend about Toader's staff, your cousin said they used to call him Moses in the village."

"Moses or the Archbishop, and she was the Crow - people were astonished that my mother, a girl of sixteen, would walk around dressed in black all the time - *to koritsi me to mavro* - and with a staff..."

"What did you just say? I didn't understand."

"I said, a girl dressed in black carrying a staff taller than she was..."

"So when the family came, Grandfather went into hiding. And who appeared at the gate with the staff in her hand, but Grandmother..."

"With a stake, not with the staff. The old thief told her in no uncertain terms that she had to go home. That the joke had gone too far, that he had spoken to the Metropolitan about getting the marriage to this penniless blockhead annulled - that he was taking her back with him, even in her state - pregnant, that is. Mother said no: she'd left home and that was how it was going to stay, and that they'd be better off going back to where they'd come from. The old thief said that if she stayed with Popescu, he wouldn't give her an inch of land. Mother said she had enough land as it was, her penniless blockhead had five hectares, and even if his land was only a tiny drop in a very large ocean, she still wouldn't accept stolen land... That was when the argument started: Gheorghe, Mother's brother, lashed the cat-o'-nine-tails over the fence, from his horse, caught her by the legs and started dragging her..."

"With what? A cat-o'-nine-tails is a whip, not a lasso."

"One and the same around our way. The cowherds, our cowboys, flick it in a certain way and the end of the whip curls up and winds around your legs - and then they pull..."

226

"Did he want to drag Grandmother over the fence?"

"He only wanted to steal her feet out from under her - thief that he was, that Gheorghe. But it didn't work, Mother knew about the cat-o'-nine-tails, the 'technique' and the taste of it. Her brother had once given her a hiding with it, in the Court, in front of the servants..."

"What 'technique'?"

"If you didn't want to be pulled down or dragged along, you wouldn't pull yourself away, you moved into it, with it, then the whip became slack, undid itself, and you got away... And so Mother didn't get caught by it, opened the gate and said to her brother: 'You wanted to whip me with the cat-o'-nine-tails, so get down from your horse and come get me: you use the cat-o'-nine-tails and I'll use the stake.' "

"What language were they speaking in?"

"Huh! What language?" Mother got annoyed. "I don't know, I wasn't there. I hadn't even been born - Mother told me the story in Romanian, at any rate."

"And so they actually fought it out, brother and sister?"

"And so what? It was a clean fight."

"Clean, he with a cat-o'-nine-tails and she with a stake! Grandmother would have won, of course."

"Of course, of course she did, what else could have happened? First, she swung at him with the stake and split his head open, and made a mess of one of his hands, but then she really showed him..."

"And? What did she do?" - I urged her, even though I knew anyway, I'd already heard this part of the story.

"And then she shouted ("in a *very* loud voice", I filled in), 'Toa-derrr! Bring on the bees!' "

"The bees?" (I asked, for form's sake, me being the listener).

"And he came running with a beehive and slammed it down in front of the gate. When the Greeks saw that the beehive had broken open..."

(Where had I read that before? In Heroditus? Or in

Creanga? It didn't really matter - perhaps I hadn't at all, but it was a good one in any case.)

"...they jumped onto their horses and made a bolt for it, their heels were sizzling..."

"Their hooves, you mean," I corrected.

"What? Oh yes, their hooves," Mother sighed, letting herself sink into her pillow, closing her eyes.

We finished the story another time, during another visit.

"But the family didn't give up, did they?" I said. "They came back again later, wearing masks to protect their faces."

"They came back all right. But by then Mother and Father were ready for them with long whips and cat-o'-nine-tails, and with burrs..."

Oh yes. The burrs...I knew what they were: the spiky fruit of wayside and meadow thistles, about the size of peas with needle-sharp hooks which were slightly poisonous... So my grandparents at Chistelnita had tied the burrs onto the ends of the cat-o'-nine-tails and then whipped the horses, but only where they were sensitive - I'm sure I've read that somewhere before. And the horses, of course, maddened with the pain, started and bolted away...

"They brought that Greek to shame, Lord, did they bring him to shame!" chuckled Mother, her hand over her mouth. "They kept on trying though, either in a roundabout way or directly, but it was getting a bit late to take her back. Mother was well along in her pregnancy - she was having me - still the old thief wouldn't give up. He couldn't take her back any more, but he wasn't going to let her get on with her life in peace.

"He thought money could buy anything. He bought land or took it by force, until he had everything bordering our five hectares... Mother had built herself a watch-tower and looked out from there with the stake and other weapons of hers... And one day, along came the old thief with two officials from Orhei - from the County Court or property survey office, Lord knows who they were. And they waved a document in front of Mother's face, according to which, they said, three hectares of our arable land...belonged to him, he'd bought them...

"Mother said: 'Really! Let me have a look at those papers.' She took them and was reading them and I don't know how, but just then Father shouted out to her to move as fast as she could because Dumana had got into the vineyard. So Mother ran to catch the cow. And returned with her on the end of a rope..."

"Dumana, that was the one who ate the clothes off the washing-line?"

" That was the one. A good cow - and not only for milk... Mother told the officials: 'This good-for-nothing cow, she tore the papers right out of my hand, but if you can wait for a few hours, she'll pass them back to you...' The old man was furious and scorched the side of her face with his hand..."

Mother felt the blow herself - she raised her hand to her cheek and closed her eyes.

"And then she grew just a bit angry - yes, he'd insulted her... Well, and then..."

And then the battle started - not a fight between them, father and daughter, but the force of good overcoming evil.

"Lord! She really gave him a thrashing! Loorrdd! Mother really brought that old thief to shame!"

My mother was beaming, as radiant as the sun, lying in the hospital bed where she was dying, dying a little bit more every day, but she wouldn't give in.

I learned the other half of the story, from the opponent's point of view, from her cousin, my "uncle". However, he didn't talk of the shame she'd brought on him, but rather of the "disgrace of the family".

"Your grandmother was the disgrace of the family!" he shouted, pointing his finger towards the ceiling. "And she was stupid: to give up the wealth, the esteem - and for what?"

"What for?" I helped him on.

"For a...to give up the land, the houses, the mills, the pharmacies, to go after a penniless blockhead! Can you believe it?"

"I know..." I said. "Especially when you think she could have had the pharmacies as well. But as for the penniless blockhead, let's leave that out of it, otherwise I'll land myself in the middle of a class war..."

"But really though: she left our home, the Court, behind; she left..."

"...those pharmacies..."

"...yes, and the pharmacies behind, and what for, to end up milking cows! And to gather eggs from the chickens - her, with her own hands!"

"No!" I said indignantly. "What, she, in person, my grandmother, milked cows! With her own hands - but that's in-ad-mis-si-ble!"

My second cousin gave me a sidelong glance and watched me carefully for a while. Was I being serious? Or was I making fun of him? And then:

"I saw it with my own eyes: she was milking a cow!"

"Seriously? She was milking a poor cow? But what do you do then, in that Greece of yours, how do you get the milk from a cow? Oh, yes: you lot, in that Greece of yours, you don't have cows, you keep goats - well, how do you get the milk out of the goats? Don't tell me, let me guess: you tie it up by the horns to an olive tree, split its udder open and after the goat's spilled out all of its...milk, you close it up again and put it out to graze..."

My second cousin was starting to find it difficult to laugh:

"A joke's a joke, but I was being serious."

"So was I. Do you Greeks know any other way of milking a cow other than with your hands?"

"What do you keep saying 'you Greeks' and 'that Greece of yours' for? I'm not Greek! But if that's the way you want

230

to play it, you're Greek as well!"

"I am whatever I want to be."

Pardon? Where on earth did I get that from? I must have read it somewhere and liked the sound of it. But that's how it is: I'm Greek, Macedonian, Polish, and what else might I be? Russian, Gypsy, Serbian, Tartar, Bulgarian... That's why I'm Romanian as well. Because I can say to myself, my mother tongue's Romanian - okay. But I wonder what my mother's mother tongue was: Greek or Romanian? Greek or Romanian - it ended up being only Romanian, because Mother didn't speak Greek, only a few lines she knew off by heart, but she didn't know what those lines meant. And Father, he didn't know a word of Polish - why not? Were the Romanians so overpowering that they completely assimilated the non-Romanians within a generation or two? Not all of them, though, but Greeks are the easiest people to assimilate - especially in the country... Am I sure about that? No, I'm not, how many country-Greeks do I know? Fair enough, I found out rather late that I was Greek as well - but even then, I didn't feel the slightest need to learn Greek - why not? Out of laziness, in the first place. And secondly, out of... shame. Is that right or not? Well yes, roughly, even though there's nothing shameful about having Greek blood in you. But look how things end up when we're of mixed blood: we're ashamed, we try to hide it and, in order to be taken for true natives (for we are true-born natives ourselves), we insult the others, especially the ones from whom we... Yes, even we ourselves... Like Mother, who kept calling them fat Greeks, thieving Greeks; or like me, now, trying to get out of it by turning the tables on someone else... And I've always been trying to...

"I've got nothing against you..." I resumed.

"That's just what your grandfather said when he left! The story about the milking - we'll let that be, but do you know what state she ended up in, after she'd gone off with Popescu?"

"What state did she end up in, sir?" (Once again, I felt more secure in the role of Grandmother's defender, defender of the...non-Greeks, that is.)

"She went around barefoot, man! Barefoot! Have you ever heard the like! From my very own family..."

"What do you mean, man, barefoot!" I was astonished myself. "But that's a crime: *lèse-Grecque*, man - sorry, *Kir Iani**..."

"What crime? And what was that you said?"

"It doesn't matter, it's an unforgivable crime in any case," I was letting myself be driven by old prejudices. "My grandmother obviously ignored the fact that the mental agility, the language and the skills of the Greek all reside in his shoes - what is the Greek for those national sandals you wear?"

My second cousin wasn't keeping up with me. He just said:

"How should I know - if I'm not Greek myself... And I've never worn sandals. We men wear knee boots, and our women wear lace-up ankle boots."

"Knee boots... You go around in boots? Summer as well?"

"Even in the summer we went around with something on our feet, man, not barefoot like that Holban's son Popescu in Chistelnita! But what are you asking me for, anyway?"

I still don't know, clearly, but I know that I'll find out one day.

"Well," I said, "it could well be that the real reason for Grandmother running away from that Court of yours, from the wealth and es-te-e-em, was the smell."

"The smell?"

My second cousin wasn't a very good sparring partner for this conversation, his forte was the monologue.

"Yes, man," I said. "The stench. Of the family."

---

* *Kir Iani* - Greek for "Sir Ion".

232

"What stench... How dare you?! What do you mean, what...smell did our family have?"

"Of money and privilege, isn't that so?" I said. "And because Grandmother had a normal sense of smell, she couldn't bear..."

"What couldn't she bear? What stench?"

"Of feet. In summer. In boots, man."

Silence. I'd won. I'd wiped him out. And rather easily. How good I'd have been as an Archangel defending the Romanian people - against all these foreigners, you understand. But the fat Greek wouldn't give up:

"How do you know our feet smelled? Did Popescu, your grandfather tell you?... who must have found out when he was kissing our boots!"

What was I saying? The non-Romanian, the foreigner comes into our country, the Romanian's country, barefoot and with his knapsack on a stick and, after a few years, there he is with boots on, riding over the poor Romanian. And even forcing him to kiss boots - *his* boots, him, the foreigner, the village leech! I would have been so good as a fascist or as a member of the Iron Guard - but it wasn't to be, even though I met all the requirements. And even the external ones, if I can call them that, including the name - Grandmother's un-nameable name... But because I'd missed the boat, historically (only because of my age, not because of anything else), I've had to console myself with a certain sense of humour... So, then, I said:

"No, Grandfather didn't tell me. I found out from Grandmother, when she used to grow capsicums!"

And with that, I wiped him out completely. The fat Greek with the sharp nose - which was no longer as sharp as it had been ... cried, even yelped:

"Get out! Get out of this house immediately!"

"With the greatest of pleasure, sir - and when did you say you were going to visit Mother in the hospital? Just once would be more than enough."

"I will, I will... But if she starts going on again with all her..."

"She doesn't start them any more," I said. "She finishes them now."

My second cousin couldn't understand. That crowned it all.

kept tight hold of my two...) That was why we had to have peace and quiet if we were to be able to work: Old Iacob put the base down in the middle of the courtyard and crowned it (the base of the barrel) with three or four concentric circles - it depended how big the barrel was going to be - and said:

"Ssssh! We mustn't make a sound..."

On tiptoe (Old Iacob always took his boots off when he was working on anything to do with barrel-making), he went over to the fence of the flower garden, where countless staves were lined up; picked one of them up and tip-tiptoed his way back... He put the stave on end, in between the outside edge of the base and the inner circle, and beckoned me over his shoulder to come closer and hold it in place - but Ssssh, quietly, we mustn't make a sound... On tiptoe, I came closer and closer and took hold of the stave, my heart pounding: was my heart making too much noise? Old Iacob, still on tiptoe, skipped over, as light as a feather, with the second stave - I had to hold onto that one as well. When the third one came, things began to get complicated; I only had two hands - but nobody set Old Iacob's back up, did they? He propped the third one up with a hazel rod; and the fourth, and all the others until we'd made "the flower".

" An' now, f'rgive th' language, but let's pull its skirt up a littl' bit... But, quiet! Don't make a sound..."

He pulled the staves together, and then putting his hands under the hazel sticks, slowly lifted the smallest circle and somehow fixed it onto the staves with the claw of his hammer; then he did the same with the second circle, bringing it higher up than the first one, further up the staves, which made the petals close a little bit. He had to go around the barrel two or three times, crouching all the time, until the staves would stand up by themselves...

"Sssh, not a sound when I'm puttin' the crown on..."

And we worked together on this as well: we both went to get another circle - in reverse order, starting with the biggest one - and tiptoed over to the flower. And crowned it. And

Old Iacob said:

"It's the Pope wearin' 'is three crowns all on top of each other..."

When we put the last crown in place (which was only just resting on the ends of the staves), Old Iacob, who was now swimming in sweat, whispered:

"Well, my littl' lad, now's th' time for th' lid. It'll be as hard as puttin' a lid on that woman's mouth, Domnica, th' martyr of Chizdruieni..."

The lid was the base at the other end. It was already prepared, with three little nails stuck into it, just long enough to be hooked around to secure the lid in place. It was an operation I didn't help him with - only from a distance. Because, as the old man said, it was "very, very delicate". Only once did the lid fall into the inside of the barrel - and when it did, the old man breathed in very, very deeply and said to me:

" 'Ere, you go over home, my boy, an' come back in a bit - but make sure you close th' door well an' good behind you, so you don't 'ear what I've got t' say t' this thing 'ere..."

To say. To tell it off, he meant. The lid which had fallen inside. I did go home but I didn't shut the door behind me. And so I heard it. The longest poem I'd ever heard made out of swear words; or poetic swearing - they even rhymed as well.

When the barrel was knitted together, I mean the lid was fastened in place, Old Iacob said:

"We got out o' a scrape there, th' pair of us - let's celebrate with a rolly full o' baccy!"

And I had my part to play in this, as well. I ran into the house, got out a crock (a conical pitcher with a widely-flared lip, the size of a bowl, perfect for what I had to do) and went down into the cellar. I filled it up with wine and returned to him, holding it with both hands, my elbows pressed into my armpits to carry the weight.

"God thank you, my littl' friend..."

240

Old Iacob put the "rolly" he'd already made, but hadn't yet lit, on the edge of his cigarette box, took hold of the crock with both hands and drank. And smacked his lips. Then he lit his rolly, drew on it and after drew on the crock as well. I knew what he could take: a litre and a half. Old Iacob used another form of measurement: two rollies to the crock - in about half an hour...

"Fine, but where's all th' nectar gone to?" he'd say, patting his stomach.

When he said that - the old man held the crock up to the light, turned it upside down and then looked inside - I knew that the dance was going to start. And so I jumped back over the stile to our house, went up onto the *calidor* and waited.

Old Iacob pushed his hat further back on his head and picked up the wooden hammer and the "snake's mouth" - a kind of tool which was hollowed out lengthways and which he used for beating out the iron hoops. I'd seen many coopers doing this, and was to see many more, but none of them were ever like Old Iacob. All the others beat out the circles: that was all. But Old Iacob...

Before he even started in with the "snake's mouth", he got into a rhythm - his whole body moved with it, especially his feet, beating out the rhythm on the ground. After he'd got warmed up, he went over to the barrel, knocking the hammer against the "tail" of the "snake": then moved up to the barrel, and back again; then, from four paces away, struck a glancing blow; back to the beginning again, forwards, backwards, then a glancing blow from two paces away - and forwards and backwards again. For a while...a long while, Old Iacob didn't actually strike the hoop - which, in principle, he was supposed to be beating. You might have said that he was trying to tame it, make it dizzy - before the beating. The beating with the hammer and the snake, and then pauses countered by short grunts, bellows really, like my morning greetings.

But I got dizzy first. A special kind of dizziness that I'd

241

worked myself into, helped, it's true, by the knock-knocking, the shuffling of bare feet in the dust of the courtyard, and the he-ha-ho's of Old Iacob.

If my parents were at home, they came out onto the *calidor* to watch as well. And, if there were any people passing by, they stopped as if glued there. If lessons were being held, everyone was given a recreation period and the children rushed to the windows (usually the old man "danced" when there weren't any lessons, but you never knew...).

Because I was the cooper's assistant, I knew that Old Iacob didn't really need to tame the iron circle on the barrel like that, it could have been finished quite quickly. But Old Iacob was Old Iacob. The barrel wasn't what counted, something else did; and not necessarily the dance, but rather the dancer. And the audience.

My Old Iacob was a spoon-maker as well. In the area around Mana at least, spoon-making wasn't monopolised by the Gypsies (moreover, there were very few Gypsies around our way - one tinker to a village - but since Mana wasn't classed as a village, it didn't have any at all...) and people carved their own spoons, ladles, scoops and even troughs themselves - and always in winter time...

And in the caravanserai he had stacks of different kinds of wood drying out, to use for making different things. I'd never seen him chiselling out a trough (although he had started one before I was born, but hadn't got round to finishing it yet...), but I had seen him carving spoons... First of all, he spread all his tools out on the ground - he had lots of them, he'd made them all himself, but he didn't use them all because they were so ... beautiful - then he picked up a piece of wood:

"Well then, what d' you want this t' end up as, lad? A spoon for fish soup with a leaf o' lovage, a pinch o' pepper and *mamaliga*? Or a spoon for a borsch made o' cabbage an' smoked pork? Or d'you want it t' end up as a pan-spoon, for stirrin' calves kidneys up wi' lots o' onion, 'n' flamed in a drop o' white gin? But no...you're a bit too small 'n' you'd burn your fingers in th' fire - wouldn't you rather a jam-spoon, 'specially for my littl' lad so's 'e can eat cherry jam, not walnut or apricot, but cherry, I said, that your Aunt Domnica made on St Mary's day 'n' put away. But don't worry...we'll find it, 'n' you'll soon be waggin' your littl' tail..."

And Lord above (as Creanga would say), the miracles he made with his hands! And not only the "tails" - the handles were carved with coiled snakes, fish with open mouths, birds, ivy, flowers, sometimes even "bodies" (but they were always dressed, Old Iacob's sirens always had something draped around their hips, so you couldn't even tell they had them), but the spoons themselves were miraculous - the other spoon-makers handled them as if they were saintly relics. And Old Iacob made them "by the mouth": spoons for right-handed people, spoons for left-handed people, for the mouth of a child, for the mouth of an old woman... At least that's what he meant them to be. It wasn't important how they turned out, the important thing was what he said they were going to be...and he made a little hole in the end of every handle: "So's you can hang it round yer neck, or from yer belt," he said.

The iron hoops for Old Iacob's barrels were all the same to me. But the hazel wood ones were special...because I *worked* on those. First and foremost, the hazel wood had to be brought back from the forest. I used to go into the forest with Old Iacob, at least when there was the chance of the hazelnuts being ready to eat...

I'd start to get ready a few days beforehand. The night before, Mother would put some things into a knapsack for me, first the medicines: a bottle of spirit, another of iodine, and in a box, snake ointment which a blind pedlar used to sell every spring. Only "gentlemen" bought it; the peasants healed their bites with spells, and healed the snake "burns" with a red-hot iron straight from the fire...

(To this day I haven't been able to establish any scientific explanation for "snake burns", which I'd seen on the soles of children's feet in Mana and even once had one myself: "What is it, why are you limping, have you got a thorn in your foot?" "No. I trod on a snake, look, here's the burn." And sure enough, they'd show the burn on the sole of their foot: a strip, sometimes narrow, other times about two-fingers' breadth, where the skin was blistered. "Does it hurt?" "It burns and itches," the victim would reply. Some claimed they'd seen the snake they'd carelessly trodden on - it was a lie! If you saw the snake first, it couldn't burn you; and if you killed it afterwards... Usually you didn't realise what had happened until the next day - 'cause, well, that's what snakes are like around here... That's what happened to me: the sole of my foot was itching and burning; I sat on the ground and wiped my foot clean with some reeds; there was a strip of skin whiter than the rest - the burn.

(It was pointless Mother trying to tell me that it was just superstition: that there weren't any poisonous snakes around our way, not even lizards or any other reptilian monsters with poisonous skin that burned your feet - because if all the children in the whole of Mana knew that there were such snakes, there must have been! And so, because there were, it had to be healed in the proper way. You heated an iron red-hot in the fire and burned the burn - simple!

(It was even more pointless Mother trying to tell me, with the help of a few slaps on the face, that the primitives who lived in Mana probably burned their feet by stepping on a hot iron in the first place, then claimed that they'd trodden on a snake - and had to burn themselves again, this time, they said, so that it would heal - I can't remember anything at all, nothing at all, about what and how I did it, because you had to do it by yourself, and even if there were children standing around the fire, they had to move back, or turn their heads away when you took the iron out of the red-hot coals, then you had to take a deep, deep breath, clench your teeth and bring your foot up to... Well, I burned my foot as well, but only to heal the snake burn.)

And so, Mother prepared my little knapsack, and early in the morning we had a good breakfast, I picked up my little bowl and axe and both of us crossed the stile into Old Iacob's.

"Old Iacob, make sure you look after the boy, don't let him get bitten by any snakes, don't let him eat any poisonous berries, make sure he doesn't disturb any wasps' nests, don't let..."

"Do you really think it likely, Missus? No, Lady, th' boy's safe wi' me..."

"Well don't say I haven't warned you! And if you bring him back bitten or stung or scratched or poisoned or cut or..."

"D'you think it likely, Missus?"

Anyway, Mother rattled her lines off nineteen to the dozen - but really, where did I usually go when I didn't have classes - wasn't I in the fields, down by the stream or in the forest? But that was her role as a mother, wasn't it?...

And so we set off, well-behaved and very well-equipped. We had our shoes on, that is. But, as soon as we left the village, before we even reached the forest, Old Iacob ordered:

"Right! Equipment off!"

And we took our shoes off. Well, he took his shiny knee boots off, the ones with the high heels. I took my sandals off. Both of us tied them onto pieces of string we'd brought with us especially for that purpose and slung them over our shoulders like scrips. Yes, that was the way to look like you were going on a long journey...

When we got into the forest, Old Iacob said:

"Well, just you take a look at that there tree, my littl' lad! That's a maple! That's what we call it, 'cause we say:

Rub th' maple, 'n' carve a table!... That one there's a sycamore. You call it sycamore, 'cause we say chipa-sticka-sycamore, on th' floor or for th' door!... An' look at that one, over there, all dappled 'n' smellin' so good! That's a lime! We call it lime, 'cause we say: Linden-lime, sweet 'n' fine, pick your tools 'n' take your time!... An' that one there's hornbeam..."

"So why do you call an oak tree an oak, Old Iacob?"

Nobody could catch my Old Iacob out. He scratched his head under his hat, and then said:

"In times o' old, they used t' call it an ork, but in them days, th' folk were lazy, 'n' they met at th' ork for a talk... An' so they changed it to oak, 'n' now, they say that if you meet at th' oak , there's no time to smoke... Y'understand?"

"I understand. But what about the elm, why do they call it the elm?"

"That's what they call it now, boy, but they used t' use it t' build th' old galleons, but people are lazy ... helm - 'elm...'"

"And what about the pine, why do they c..."

"Where can you see a pine 'round 'ere? There are no pines at all in Orhei Forest, those are mountain trees."

"Well, why do they call them pines over there, in the mountains?"

"That's their business, only they can tell you that. But I met a mountain-man once, in Orhei, at th' fair, 'n' he said they 'ad so many pines, they ran out o' numbers 'n' 'ad t' use all th' nines; 'n' they said: Time's fine t' chop th' pines, chisels out t' carve th' nines - but I don't know if 'e was lyin' t' me or not..."

"And the beech, Old Iacob, what about the beech?"

"You'll not find a beech 'round our way, but they must call it that 'cause sittin' underneath th' beech is a fine young girl, pretty-as-a-peach."

"Hmhmm! And the elder?"

"Sittin' underneath th' elder's a fine young girl 'n' you call 'er Zelda."

And so we went on, until we got to the hazel tree.

"And what about the hazel tree, why do you call it hazel?"

"That's because it's so tall: you can't even get t' th' end o' th' word 'n' your gaze runs out because o' this haze, hazel-haze-gaze - d' you understand?"

How could I not understand what Old Iacob told me?

Before we got down to work, we had something to eat. Old Iacob made a fire in a clearing. He took all the big and heavy things out of his knapsack: a handful of potatoes (Aunt Domnica would be nagging, because he must have pulled up at least ten plants, they were so tiny, like little peanuts), four or five ears of sweet corn... And, of course, his swig - a litre bottle of wine. But he didn't open that, not yet anyway.

He left me to look after the fire and went for a walk. The flames hadn't even taken hold of the twigs by the time he came back - his hat full of mushrooms and with a clove of garlic - wild onion.

We roasted the potatoes, corncobs and the mushrooms. We ate things in the order they were ready - the corn with bread, the garlic with the mushrooms... I drank water from my bowl, he helped himself to swigs of wine...

After we'd eaten, we set to work. We looked for the straightest and tallest hazels - we couldn't even see the tops for the haze...

We chopped them down, without splitting them when we felled them, stripped all the leaves off and stacked them; I put the single hazelnuts I'd pulled off for myself to one side and the clusters of nuts to another, even if they weren't quite ripe. When Old Iacob said the sun was right in the middle of the sky, he sounded tools-down on his bugle. And it was lunchtime.

We lit the fire again and had something to eat - but we didn't have much of an appetite: we were sleepy.

"Don't sleep with your mouth open, or a snake might slip

in," he recommended, quite seriously.

I knew why - and I wasn't afraid. Because I knew how to make the snake come out again as well: you warmed a pan of milk and put it next to the man the snake had gone into, who had to sit with his mouth wide open over the pan of milk so that the smell of the milk would go right inside and into the snake's nostril and, because the horrible creatures loved milk (we'd all seen them on cows' udders, hanging down from the teats, - but people didn't kill them if the cows hadn't been milked because it soothed their udders), the snake would come out - only somebody had to be watching, with his hands at the ready around the man's mouth, and when the hideous thing poked its head out you had to grab it by the throat and pull it out - but not too hard in case it snapped inside or you tore the man's insides, you had to pull slowly, very slooooowly...

We went back home, pulling the "sleigh" Old Iacob had built to carry the wood. But I wasn't interested in this bit. I was waiting for the day when we could chop the wood and make circles out of it - Old Iacob measured them with string, very precisely, marked them, then cut them - I held on to them... Anyway, that was the forest finished with - for a while...

Old Iacob had a patch of vineyard as well, over towards the west. He took me up there with him, once at the end of spring, when the vines were in flower, once again on St Mary's day, when the fruit was starting to show, and twice in autumn, before the grapes were picked.

Heaven must smell like that: like the hills in Mana when the vines are in blossom. They don't say for nothing: *When the blossom's on the vine, then shall St Mary here recline* - and I'd seen, with my very own eyes (not in the company of Old Iacob, but with the other children), young men and girls chasing each other through the vines, naked, like Adam and Eve - that's what people said when they had no clothes on;

and I'd also heard, with my very own ears, the giggling and the laughing and the singing and the loud moaning. The first time I saw naked people running after each other in the vineyards, shrieking, I thought they were hitting each other. I asked one of the bigger boys I was with:

"What might they be doing, I wonder?" (I spoke very correctly, like at school.)

"Wha d'you think?" replied my friend who was much older than I was, he was about twelve... "They're lyin' down..."

"What do you mean, lyin' down?" I said, confused. "But look at them, they're running about chasing each other, hitting each other..."

"They always do that at th' beginnin'. An' after they've finished th' beginnin' bit, they go and lie down. Lie down, they go lyin' down, lad, like girls lie down with lads, a man with a woman, your Dad with your Mum - 'ave you never seen you Mum lyin' with your Dad?"

"No, because the Russians pulled Dad in..." So that was why I hadn't known what people meant when they said lying down - even though I'd already been doing it, but it was so nice it didn't need a name.

I'm still convinced that of all the flowers and sweet-smelling herbs which grew and blossomed around those parts, not one of them could compare with the vine-blossoms. Perhaps each flower by itself didn't give off such a good smell, or even none at all, but a hillside of them ... hillsides ... the sweet vines ... or sweet childhood?

On St Mary's Day I went up to the hills with Old Iacob, to the vineyards to see if the grapes had appeared yet.

But I've already told that story. No I haven't, not all of it. Only the beginning.

But what about the others, other stories to start telling, so many of them...

What's the point in, well, everything? I mean, I left there

but it seems like I've never even been there, as if I've got no beginnings to start.

I wanted to tell the story of the grape-picking; and then about the pressing; and then all about the young wine; and after that, the story about bringing the corn in, after it had been snowing, and about lying down at harvest time - where you lay down and all the different kinds of lying down, like this and like that, and even like this - and the story about winter in the back lane and in the cherry orchard and all the branches and about Creanga, who'll be a part of me and of us, for ever and always.

And I would have liked to have talked about my grandparents - Grandmother at Ciocalteni and my grandparents at Chistelnita and how I was scared of the windmill which I thought was the Devil and how I cut my foot open on a hoe and how. And how. And how.

And how I didn't like autumn.

But how I did like Valentina, the priest's older daughter, because she could draw really well and painted the entrance to the church, on the walls, in colour, *The-Romanian-soldier-with-his-bayonet* and/or *-at-Dalnic*, where there had been only crosses and helmets. I held the paints and didn't dare look up, because if I'd looked up at her on the ladder, I would have seen that she had pink or blue or lilac panties on - it depended. I don't know what it depended on, but it was so important that if I can't remember what Valentina's face looks like now, I can certainly remember (today) what the scar was like above her right knee.

And I can still remember. And I can. And I.

And - nothing. Because we had to leave.

And when you leave, you die, that's what they say.

The Departure

On the *calidor* of the house in Mana. For the last time. I
didn't know exactly what that meant: the-last-time, even
though I was, well, nine years old *and* five months - well,
not quite five, but definitely four. Not even Mother knew.
She couldn't even guess.

Mother picked up one of our things. And wrapped it.
Tried to find a place for it in the bags. Then took it out
again. Put it back in its place.

"You can stay here!" Mother said. "You stay right here,
and wait for us!"

In between going into and coming out of the courtyard-
house-school, Father would remind Mother:

"Don't forget to take..." and said the name of whichever
thing.

From the *calidor* I could see Mother inside the house,
perfectly. Once, then once more, she stroked the object
she'd just taken out of the baggage to put back in its rightful
place. And to wait for us there. She even took one thing
out after Father had shouted not to forget it.

"How could I forget that?" she said, offended, rummaged
around in the baggage, found it, and put it to one side: "You
can stay here! Stay right here and wait for us, do you
understand? And you!" she shouted to Father. "What are
you doing about the waggoners? Can't you hear the
cannon?"

Oh, yes: the cannon, I'd forgotten. If Mother hadn't
brought it to our attention, we wouldn't even have noticed
it. Even though when it boomed and puffed and spluttered,
the windows rattled. We had got used to the windows and
the cannon. For about ten days it had been "burping" over

251

towards the right. That's where east was. People were saying: beyond the river Dniester.

From here, from the *calidor*, you could see people easily. You could easily see the people from the village. All of a sudden they had become hard-working. And you couldn't usually say that about the people around here, in Mana. They were going to and fro up to the hill and back. And if you want to know how many times - about four-five-or-six times a day. From the crack of dawn they started moving their cattle and ploughs. Even old Morcov was whisking about yesterday in the back lane, with a reaper which wasn't being pulled by horses as it should have been, but by oxen. They didn't have anything to do in the hills any more. They hadn't for a long time. The autumn wheat was growing all by itself; the spring wheat had already been sown. It wasn't time for the corn or the potatoes yet - that was later, after Easter. What Easter? To hell with Easter from now on, Father said.

From here, from the *calidor*, you could easily see the people in Mana. But they couldn't see their own heads, they had so much on their shoulders. Hammering and knocking in the courtyards, walking around to the neighbours' to ask for a tool or a bit of advice. They hadn't had anything to mend unless they'd broken something themselves since the snow had melted; just to give themselves something to do, they were making, repairing and adjusting everything. But we hadn't heard the cannon before the snow melted.

Between his comings and goings, Father would ask his neighbours, rather than walk around in silence:

"How are you doing, Gheorghe (or Vasile, or Ilie), aren't you collecting your things together?"

"Well, I'm goin' to, of course. Can't leave 'em lyin' about, can I? But I'll 'ave to 'ave a good think about it first," Gheorghe replied, scratching his head under his fur cap for enlightenment. But I didn't think he was telling the truth: the man laughed quietly for a long time; and his eyes went small just like when you play a trick on somebody -

somebody stupid who asks you, stupidly, a stupid question.

Father wouldn't insist. In fact, before he'd got half way through the question, he had his back turned to the man he had spoken to and was getting on with his own business.

"Haven't you changed your mind, Old Iacob?" Father shouted, just as indifferently, over the fence.

"Well, th' Lord's good, Teacher-Sir, he won't forsake us, not Him, not even this time. Anyway, at our age, where are we goin' t' go, with a knapsack on th' end o' a stick? Good or bad, this's my house; better or worse, this's my land 'n' th' place I know - where am I going to go to, wanderin' 'round like an 'omeless Jew? An' th' Russian's human as well, 'n' if we take it gently when he's around...'cause we're all men t'gether..."

"That's the long and short of it, Old Iacob", said Father on the point of walking away. But then he turned around:

"Well, you know, it's not quite like that, Old Iacob. I'm scared that this time we won't all act like men - neither us, nor them. You know the Muscovites, and you've had a little taste of the Soviets, but that's not enough. And you only knew them when they were withdrawing - what happened around here in '41. But that was like taking candy from a baby compared to what it's going to be like, because they're advancing now. I've seen the way they've advanced, in their own country - but when they're coming to take care of someone else's country...

"Look, let's say that they come over the hill, there; and here, in the valley, we have only one point of resistance left, a machine gun in the church belfry... Well, what would a Romanian or a German do in their position? It would break his heart, but he'd aim directly at the belfry! He might even use a cannon, it wouldn't be the first time, but only on the belfry, because that's where the resistance is. A Russian's tactics are different though: he gets the cannon out. A hundred, two hundred, as many as he's got - he lines them all up, as if it were a parade, and fires. Straight in front of him. For an hour, a day, three days and nights. And if a shell hits the belfry as well, fine! If it doesn't, it's still fine by him, because the tactics of the Russians aren't to gain as much as they can from as few means as possible."

"Well, Teacher-Sir, all tactics 're the same t' me, war's war, who takes us into account, us civilians? But He won't forsake us, not Him, th' Lord, He'll help us t' get through this ordeal..."

Father didn't insist. The man was right: where could Old Iacob go at his age? He might have been mayor of the village but he was still a peasant. And where was a peasant supposed to go: move onto another peasant's land? It was all accounted for, it didn't stretch if you pulled it at both sides. The Teacher-Sirs of the village, they worked for the State, they'd received documents and travel papers for themselves and their families, and other paperwork as well, they'd had them for a good week; they knew where they were coming from and where they were going to end up: the village Gusu, commune of Ludos, region of Sibiu, Transylvania; that would be their journey, theirs and their possessions - free, the State was paying - but what about them, the peasants? They had neither salaries nor travel papers, where could they go? And with what? Nobody'd be waiting for them at the end of their journey with a cup of tea and a slice of bread and marmalade and nobody'd be there to put them up - what could they do, among strangers? We might have all spoken the same language, we might all have been called Romanians, but we were still strangers if we weren't from the same village... But don't worry, the Lord was merciful, He wouldn't forsake us, not Him...

The Lord was merciful and this time everything for our taking refuge was well-organised: civil servants received "relocation announcements " in good time, to the provinces which were...furthest away from the Russian invasion. My parents didn't "know" the area, they hadn't been there before, but since the cannon were getting closer, and were, as usual, firing straight in front, we would have plenty of time to get to know Transylvania and Sibiu. And Gusu.

Fine. So we had the documents for ourselves and for our baggage; we had the experience behind us of the last time when we didn't succeed, and of the consequences: Father being pulled in and sent to Siberia. And yet...

For a week I'd been sitting on the *calidor* watching, and seeing how we were always ready to leave but never left; how everything was being loaded, then unloaded - according to the cannon fire.

But this time, we did leave. Not because the cannon were firing any louder than yesterday, but because Father had found out from somebody he could rely on, that the Russians had broken the line at the Dniester. True, they had broken through a few days earlier but, luckily for us, they had been forced to retreat again - that was why we had unloaded everything.

And so. I was sitting on the *calidor* of the house in Mana. And I couldn't see anything apart from the oxen who'd been taken out of the yoke, standing in the middle of the courtyard next to the cart. Father couldn't find another cart drawn by horses. And so we had to leave with oxen.

And we left.

And I can't remember actually leaving. I can see myself on the *calidor*, waiting and looking at the silvery froth around the oxen's mouths. And after that, I can see myself on the road somewhere, on our journey. Walking behind the cart - so it wasn't too heavy as we went over the hill, poor oxen... But in between these two moments: nothing.

As if I didn't even get down from the *calidor*; as if I didn't say goodbye to my Old Iacob and to Aunt Domnica who was mine as well, really; or to the neighbours, to my school friends, to people in the village; as if I didn't leave the courtyard and turn around to look back at the house, our house, and at my *calidor*; at the roof of so-and-so's house, at so-and-so's walnut tree, at so-and-so's family, who'd come out to the fence to say goodbye, the men waving at us, the women sniffing into their handkerchiefs; it's as if somebody picked me up from the *calidor* when I was asleep and put me down on the gentle slope leading to Chisinau, where I was walking along behind the cart - the poor oxen.

I can't remember what time we left either. At what hour we left the house. Was it light? Or was it dark - what was it like? And when exactly were we walking behind the cart: at night? Or in the daytime? What season was it? What year?

I had been moved from the *calidor* onto the road to Chisinau. Freeze frame.

And we arrived at Chisinau. And, in Chisinau, in front of the station I saw my first tram. And inside the station walls, my first train.

Ah, the train!

The train was different from anything I'd ever known. Mainly because of the smell of it: firstly, the smell of the smoke from the coals; secondly, that particular smell, a mixture of the smell of the crude oil, red hot on the axles and the smell of rusty, burning iron (from the heat of the engine? from the sun beating down on the roofs of the compartments?); and thirdly, the smell of the third compartment.

I sat at the window of our compartment. With my elbows resting on the frame, where the window had been opened; kneeling on top of the packages in between the benches. I was looking outside at all the people, but listening to what my parents were saying inside the compartment.

And my parents weren't getting on very well at all, behind me here in the compartment. Not at all. And they were arguing - under their breath. Father said how couldn't he, he had to, look, the Russians had been forced back of the Dniester again, he had to go back home to Mana again to get some more things; and Mother said he couldn't, how could he think of leaving a woman, with a small child, alone on the train - to hell with the things! they'd still be there

256

when we returned; and Father said he didn't believe it, we wouldn't be going home all that quickly anyway and it wasn't dangerous at all: look, the Russians had been stopped, they'd even been pushed back, and even if he was to walk all the way back to Mana, he'd still get there tonight, they really couldn't go with just two packages and three suitcases, couldn't she see, couldn't Mother see, that all the others had brought their furniture as well? To hell with the furniture, what if the Russians came back quicker than he thought and got their hands on him? Hadn't once been enough for him? They wouldn't get their hands on him because, look at the map: Chisinau was here, and this was the nearest point to the Dniester and the Russians, while he, Father, would be going from Chisinau to Mana, which was north-west, so he would be in the other direction, not near the front and the Russians, just look at the map. Forget the damned map, did he really think there was any similarity between maps and how the world was these days, upside down, you couldn't rely on any maps any more, to hell with the furniture, we could make some more when we got there; if he kept on about it, soon we wouldn't be going home at all.

That's what it was like. For a long, long time, an eternity, my parents were arguing in simultaneous whispers.

When the eternity eventually came to an end, the train started moving. Only the two of us, Mother and I, were on the train. Father had gone back to Mana, north-west to get some more things, even furniture, like the other, normal people.

We travelled for a while, then the train stopped. Souvenirs-of-Iasi: pickled apples bought on the platform - with a bitter-sweet taste, wrapped in newspaper which disintegrated in our hands, sticky from the juice.

A little further on - I didn't know where, it didn't matter in any case because it wasn't Mana - the air-raid sirens. Air-raid sirens were nice in the trains for refugees: we got out of the compartments to stretch our legs a bit in the bushes which hadn't quite grown their leaves, and pretended we were hiding from the airplanes in the wheat which came up to our ankles. And then we got back in again, and again the air-raid sirens sounded, and out we got again. And then the chucka-chucka-chucka-chucka of the wheels once more and when we started feeling sick because of all the chucka-chucka, there you go, it was playtime again with the air-raid sirens and then the engine: fssss-ye, fsssss-ye and then the sccccccrreeching of the brakes and everybody-out-of-the-train and the sirens and they pretended that the bombs were dropping in front of us, but another time they were dropping behind us - I couldn't understand why we had to stop then, but I liked it when we were stopping all the time. And then we could see the air-raid. They weren't coming for us, the train, but for Ploiesti. Ah, ha, so that was the petroleum-or-crude-oil we'd learned about at school. It could burn, Petroleumandcrudeoil. It burned in lamps; it burned in engines and moved them as well; it burned really well and with very tall flames if you looked at it from a distance. The Americans, with their flying planes. We could see them clearly. They were very small, the American airplanes, but you had to be careful, they had bombs inside which were h-u-g-e. We couldn't see the huge bombs, but we could see the Petroleumand ... which was burning very brightly. And with very tall flames.

And after that it wasn't burning any more. It might have been burning over there, at Ploiesti, where Lord, Lord, look how many airplanes there were, but where we were, up in the Prahova Valley, it wasn't burning, it was chucka-chucka-ing.

I sat with Mother, next to the window.

"The air smells good around here," Mother said, breathing in very deeply, like in gym lessons.

"It's cold," I said. "It's mountain air," I told her. "Mountains are elevations in the earth's surface which were formed many years ago in our history."

Mother huddled herself up and closed the window. And said:

"Lord! but the Carpathians look all cracked! And covered in snow!"

"That's what the Carpathians are like," I said, because I knew all about geography. "The Carpathian mountains are so called because they are mountains covered in cracks and lesions."

"We're arriving in awful weather!" Mother said, trembling. "At home it was warm, the flowers were in bloom, the bees were buzzing, and it was just about time for the cuckoos to start singing, but here... It's winter here, winter..."

Sibiu. Everybody got off the train. Into winter.

How long did it take us to travel from Chisinau to Sibiu: a week? Two weeks? We were all helped onto lorries and dropped off in the courtyard of a monastery. It wasn't exactly a monastery, it was a boarding school for girls training to be teachers. But it wasn't even a boarding school now. It was the Centre. For Refugees.

We were refugees. I was a refugee.

We went to the hairdresser's - the first hairdresser to cut my hair. We went to the theatre, my first theatre; to a film, my first. We went to the station, for the first time we were on this side of the gate. So that Mother could enquire about Father. Every day we went to the station to find out about Father, sometimes several times a day. Father, no, not yet. If not today, perhaps tomorrow.

We went to the station. We were on this side, but we went through to the other side. We hadn't come for Father, we'd come for ourselves. To catch the train to a place further away, our destination, as Mother said.

We got on the train and travelled for a while. We got off. At our destination. But not quite, Mother said, leaving me to look after the baggage while she went to the station-master's to find out about our next destination, Gusu. We couldn't go on foot, there was too much baggage. We carried

259

our things into the station building.

Strange people were looking at me strangely. I explained things to them - because I knew, they didn't:

"We are refugees. I am a refugee."

These people didn't seem to be all there. Some of them nodded their heads as if to say yes, others shook their heads to say no. At the same time. Mother was busy finding out. A cart. A man with a whip.

"Ah'll take ye to Gusu - how much'll ye give me?"

"How much is it?" Mother said. "How much do you usually ask for?"

"Well then... Where have ye come from?"

"From Basarabia."

"Sooo, ye've come from a looong way awa' ?"

"We're refugees. We've been relocated to Gusu, as teachers."

"Fine! Teachers ha' got money. The r'fugees ha' got e'en more, 'cos the State has given 'em money to run away with. An' so faaaar awa' - well then, dear Lady, it'll cost ye...," and he said how much he wanted in *lei*.

Mother said it was too expensive. And that for *fifty* kilometres, from Mana to Chisinau, she'd paid half what he was asking for only ten. The man said:

"Well... but we're in the Ardeal now, not in Basarabia. Anywa', i's not the money, for ah'll be goin' back with an empty caaart anywa'. I's not the money..."

Mother only half understood - she asked him where he was going back to with his empty cart, wasn't it Gusu?

Exactly, Gusu! the man said, happy that Mother had managed to guess right, but it wasn't for the money, he didn't make his money from being a waggoner.

"Nooo, b' good-day, then!" the man said politely. He took off his hat, greeted her - and left.

There was something Mother didn't understand, but she didn't want to let me know what. Further up the road, in the late afternoon, we were in a cart. Which was going.

This man kept asking:

"B' where are ye goin' to stay in our village, in Gusu?"

"We'll find a landlady, but for the time being take me to the school, I have to talk to the headmaster."

We went on a bit further.

"B' who are ye going to stay with in our village, in Gusu?"

"We'll find somewhere - but for now, take us to the school."

Darkness.

"This is the school," the man said. "B' it's locked."

"We'll manage. Let's unload the luggage."

Mother paid and the man went off into the darkness. The three of us were left behind: Mother, myself and the baggage. Then I was left by myself, Mother went off to find things out.

She came back, late, with a lantern a man was carrying. Mother called him: "Headmaster, Sir". Headmaster-Sir called Mother: "Esteemed Colleague".

We carried the bags into the schoolyard - that's what they called it; it didn't look like a school, but you couldn't see anything anyway. Then we walked up the steps to a door, picked out from the darkness by Headmaster-Sir's lantern: the main door of the school.

Yes, it was a school all right, it smelled of schools - of waxed floorboards, and dusty floorboards, and of pupils. Even though it was the middle of the night, the school still smelled of pupils, although they never came to school at night-time but went to sleep at home, in their own beds, in their own houses.

Then we made our way with the baggage over to another door; a room which didn't have quite so strong a smell of pupils.

"Esteemed Colleague, although the law does not allow it, you will be staying here, in the office. You have everything you need here - but I'm relying on your discretion. I could be

severely punished if they found out in Sibiu that I'd put up...
Good night."

And he left. Lantern and all. We stayed behind in the darkness, but the darkness was so dark that I couldn't work out where the ceiling was, or the floor; I don't think I could even work out which was my right side. I held onto Mother's hand as tightly as I could. With both hands. My eyelids were aching, I was staring so much to try and make out something around me.

"Why didn't he leave us the lantern?" I asked, shivering.

"It's very dark in the back lane and he has to get back home quickly, they're waiting for him at dinner. I disturbed him while he was eating."

"I was in the back lane and it wasn't as dark as it is here."

"That's what it seems like to you, now. Don't worry, you'll get used to it, we'll get used to..."

"I don't want to get used to it, I want a wee," I said. "And something else, as well as a wee..."

Holding Mother's hand, we groped around to find our way out of the office, managed to get out of the office and then out of the building. We looked for The Right Place. We looked for Outside.

"Mother, I can't wait any more! I'm doing it here!"

"In the middle of the schoolyard?" Mother became furious. "The son of a teacher, thinking of something like that? And a refugee, as well. Hang on just a little bit longer, we've got to find The Right Place somewhere. Outside."

Eventually we found it. I won't say how.

"Is this how refugees do it?" I asked.

"Is what how?"

"Like this, holding someone's hand? In the darkness? And frightened? I don't like it, being a refugee. I don't want to be a refugee!"

"Let's just pretend we've gone on an excursion," Mother said.

262

"That's what the other people said, but I don't know what an excursion is and I don't want an excursion in the darkness, holding someone's hand."

We set off back to the school building. Mother said:

"Oh, I wasn't careful at all; where in God's name did I put the matches and the candles? I've got to find the matches at least, there must be a lantern in the school. There's bound to be one in the office somewhere..."

Feeling her way through the baggage, Mother found the matches. But not the candles. She used up nearly all of the sticks in the box, trying to find a lantern. Nothing.

"But what would they want a lantern in the school for?" I said. "Nobody comes to school at night-time, people don't sleep in schools at night..."

"All right, all right, don't go on, I've got the message!" said Mother, but why she was annoyed, I don't know...

We held onto each other's hands in the darkness.

"Mother, I can't wait anymore. I want to go to sleep."

"Wait until I've unfolded the blanket and spread it out."

"On the floor? What are we going to wrap ourselves up in? Or are we going to be like the Gypsies: sleep on our bellies and wrap ourselves up with our arses?"

What inspiration: letting go of Mother's hand and stepping to the side, I heard the air whistling past where my ears would have been.

"Aren't you ashamed of yourself? The son of a member of the didactic body of... and a refugee as well?"

"I'm sorry, Mother, I'll never say it again in my whole life..."

"But where are you? Where are you, for God's sake? I promise I won't smack you, but come on, back to Mama. Where are you?"

"Here. And I'm cold... What are we going to put on top of us if we sleep on top of the blanket?"

"Our overcoats. And don't worry, my little darling, I'll hold you in my arms and you'll see just how warm you'll be..."

"If you hold me in your arms and it becomes warm, will it become light as well? You know: heat makes light..."

"We don't need any light to go to sleep. In fact, science also teaches us that in the darkness, it's more restful."

We blindly lay down on the blanket spread out over the floorboards. I lay on my side so that Mother could keep my back warm.

It smelled of old tobacco.

"Mother, why did Headmaster-Sir call you: *Esteemed Colleague*?"

"Because we work in education together, we're colleagues. Because I'm a lady and that's the proper way for men to speak to ladies, men who've been brought up correctly..."

"Hmmhmmmm. Headmaster-Sir might be brought up correctly, but I'm hungry."

"If we get out of bed now and start looking through the bags, we won't be able to go to sleep. And, more than anything, sleep is what we need."

"I, more than anything, need something to make it not be so dark. And something to make me not be as hungry anymore. The darkness isn't black here anymore, it's red now, it's so dark."

"Close your eyes, and you won't see it. Tomorrow, we'll sort things out so that... Even if we have to stay in the office, we must have a lantern at least - look, Mother will buy a beautiful, new lantern... We won't be afraid of the dark anymore then - and if Father comes, we won't be afraid of anything!"

"When Father comes, will Headmaster-Sir invite us around for something to eat? I'm hungry, Mother..." and I started to cry. "I'm so huuungry..."

"Listen, my little chicken, you're a big boy now, and so you have to understand how things are: we're refugees..."

"I don't want to be a refugee - I mean, not this kind,

264

sleeping on the floor, in an office, in the dark and stretched with hunger!"

"You say: your stomach's shrunk with hunger. Or: you're dying of hunger - not stretched!"

"Well, I'm not dying and I haven't shrunk," I said. "I'm alive and I'm so hungry I feel like I've been stretched. Like I've grown. I'm stretched out long because of hunger, Mother..."

"That's enough, close your eyes! If you keep your eyes closed you won't see the darkness anymore - and it's all only because of the darkness, you know, my darling: feeling hungry and feeling homesick, everything - it's only because of the darkness. So let's close our eyes and go to sleep. And when you fall asleep, you won't feel anything any more, you won't feel hungry, or anything else. Come on, let's go to sleep, little chicken. And at least while we're asleep, let's not be refugees."

About the Translator: ANGELA CLARK is a British writer and academic, currently living and doing research in Romania for a doctorate in Romanian literature from the University of London School of Slavonic Studies.